EXERCISE AND HEALTH RESEARCH

EXERCISE AND HEALTH RESEARCH

MAGNUS D. JOHANSEN
EDITOR

Nova Science Publishers, Inc.

New York

NOTICE TO THE READER

The Publisher has taken reasonable care in the preparation of this book, but makes no expressed or implied warranty of any kind and assumes no responsibility for any errors or omissions. No liability is assumed for incidental or consequential damages in connection with or arising out of information contained in this book. The Publisher shall not be liable for any special, consequential, or exemplary damages resulting, in whole or in part, from the readers' use of, or reliance upon, this material.

Independent verification should be sought for any data, advice or recommendations contained in this book. In addition, no responsibility is assumed by the publisher for any injury and/or damage to persons or property arising from any methods, products, instructions, ideas or otherwise contained in this publication.

This publication is designed to provide accurate and authoritative information with regard to the subject matter covered herein. It is sold with the clear understanding that the Publisher is not engaged in rendering legal or any other professional services. If legal or any other expert assistance is required, the services of a competent person should be sought. FROM A DECLARATION OF PARTICIPANTS JOINTLY ADOPTED BY A COMMITTEE OF THE AMERICAN BAR ASSOCIATION AND A COMMITTEE OF PUBLISHERS.

LIBRARY OF CONGRESS CATALOGING-IN-PUBLICATION DATA
Exercise and health research / Magnus D. Johansen (editor).
  p. ; cm.
Includes bibliographical references and index.
ISBN-13: 978-1-60021-985-6 (hardcover)
ISBN-10: 1-60021-985-3 (hardcover)
 1. Exercise--Health aspects. 2. Exercise--Physiological aspects. 3. Exercise--Psychological aspects. I. Johansen, Magnus D.
 [DNLM: 1. Exercise--physiology. 2. Exercise--psychology. QT 255 E95526 2008]
RA781.E8915   2008
613.7'1--dc22   2007034248

Published by Nova Science Publishers, Inc. ✦ *New York*

CONTENTS

PREFACE

In the last 50 years significant numbers of men and women take little exercise in the course of their occupation. The computer keyboard, the rise of private transport, the world by television, household "labor saving" devices mean that with the minimal of physical effort people work and play. The benefits of doing regular exercise include a reduced risk of: heart disease, stroke, bowel cancer, breast cancer, osteoporosis, and obesity. In addition, many people feel better in themselves during and after exercise. Regular exercise is also thought to help ease stress, anxiety, and mild depression. This new book presents recent significant research from around the world dealing with various aspects and impacts of exercise as related to health.

Chapter 1 - Evolutionary psychologists have argued that there exist universally shared criteria of attractiveness, which are potent cues to a person's potential reproductive success. This article reviews the current state of evolutionary psychology's study of female and male physical attractiveness. The former focuses on body shape as measured by the waist-to-hip ratio (WHR) and body weight scaled for height, or the body mass index (BMI), whereas the latter examines the waist-to-chest ratio (WCR). The evidence seems to point to BMI being the dominant cue for female physical attractiveness, with WHR playing a more minor role. The opposite is true for male attractiveness, with WCR playing a more important role than either the WHR or BMI. Importantly, cross-cultural studies have suggested that there are significant differences for physical attractiveness in terms of body shape and weight, which evolutionary psychological arguments have difficulty in explaining. Alternative explanations and the future of the field are discussed in conclusion.

Chapter 2 - A significant progress in understanding the neurochemistry of anxiety has followed the advent of biochemical methods to induce anxiety symptoms. There has been particular interest in panic attacks since the discovery that they may be provoked in the laboratory, and thus are amenable to experimental investigation. For this reason, and because the episodic nature of a panic attack makes the disorder easy to quantify, panic disorder has been extensively studied in the last decades. Another reason why provocation of panic has attracted interest is that, in theory, knowledge gained from such studies can be extrapolated to anxiety in general. While research on the pathogenesis of panic disorder has concentrated on panic attacks, what happens to panic patients in the non-panic state has been largely overlooked. And yet, patients remain clinically unwell between attacks. Panic patients experience background anxiety and they also chronically hyperventilate. Hyperventilation was thought to induce panic by lowering CO_2, but provocation studies using carbon dioxide (CO_2) demonstrated that, in fact, panic patients have hypersensitive CO_2 chemoreceptors. Klein proposed that panic patients hyperventilate in the attempt to keep pCO_2 low, thereby preventing activation of the brain's suffocation alarm and the panic attacks that ensue. However, panic patients in the non-panic state have been shown to have EEG abnormalities, as well as abnormal cerebral blood flow and cerebral glucose metabolism, an indication of cerebral hypoxia. Hyperventilation can indeed induce cerebral hypoxia, as it leads to systemic alkalosis and cerebral vasoconstriction. Cerebral hypoxia contributes to the onset of anxiety symptoms in chronic obstructive pulmonary disease. By chronically hyperventilating, panic patients may likewise risk prolonged exposure to cerebral hypoxia which, in turn, may contribute to symptom chronicity, thereby engendering a self-perpetuating cycle of panic and anxiety symptoms. Panic patients may therefore benefit from adopting more physiological patterns of breathing. Aerobic exercise may help patients to normalise ventilatory patterns and attenuate the adverse effects of chronic hyperventilation on the brain. The role of pharmacological and psychological treatments in anxiety disorders is now well established, but there is evidence that aerobic exercise regularly is itself therapeutic in panic disorder and that it can also effectively augment antipanic treatment. Exercise may prove an adjunct treatment for anxiety disorders that is non-pharmacological, non-addictive, and one that has few adverse effects and contraindications. In addition to reducing the risk of coronary heart disease, stroke and obesity-related disorders, exercise offers a range of psychological benefits.

Chapter 3 - Psychological stress is a common aspect of modern day living and can be experienced in multiple forms that produce differing cardiovascular and immune responses. Heightened psychophysiological reactivity has been linked to unfavourable health outcomes that include cardiovascular disease, hypertension, diabetes, and sub-clinical infections. The relationship between stress-reactivity and health seems to be moderated and mediated by a number of factors such as lifestyle and genetics. One common aspect of modern living is physical inactivity and the consumption of highly refined foods lacking in essential nutrients. The purpose of this review is to highlight the role of stress-reactivity in the development of ill-health and outline the potential beneficial impact of exercise and various nutrients on the physiological response to stress, with suggestions for future directions of research. There is growing evidence supporting the stress-reactivity lowering effects of exercise and specific nutrients. These effects appear to be important for the maintenance of health in a stressful modern day environment. Although evidence pertaining to the clinical relevance of these stress-reactivity lowering effects is currently lacking, exercise and nutritional intervention should be recommended for lowering hyper-reactive responses to psychological stress.

Chapter 4 – Background: During the past two decades, Metabolic Syndrome (MetS) in the U.S. has increased to the point of being 'epidemic', primarily due to the increased prevalence of obesity. MetS is associated with increased coronary artery disease (CAD) risk. Although dietary interventions are a fundamental component of therapeutic lifestyle change (TLC) programs aimed at weight reduction, physical activity and exercise play a pivotal in reinforcing and sustaining long-term weight loss.

Methods: This article reviews and describes MetS including approaches for implementing physical activity in the context of TLC interventions. These include center- and phone-based programs as well as provider-based intervention settings.

Results and Conclusions: While TLC interventions aimed at reducing MetS are a public imperative, the most effective intervention remains to be elucidated. The various approaches used can be described as effective and having common characteristics. Further research is needed to determine the best method for reducing the risk of MetS.

Chapter 5 - Eliminating racial and ethnic disparities in coronary artery disease (CAD) risk is an important public health goal. Although Native Americans have been historically been perceived to be at low risk for CAD, recent findings indicate a high prevalence of CAD risk factors exist in this population. Much of this risk is a result of the increasing incidence of overweight/obesity that can potentially be ameliorated by lifestyle interventions aimed at weight reduction. The purpose of this article is to promote awareness that Native Americans are a high-risk CAD population and suggest strategies for lifestyle interventions aimed at obesity-related CAD risk reduction. These strategies emphasize overcoming barriers to behavioral change pertaining to dietary choices and promoting physical activity such as lack of healthy food supplies and transportation that are limited for many Native Americans. In addition, participation in total lifestyle change programs as well as individual practitioner counseling may have effective roles in reducing CAD risk among Native Americans.

Chapter 6 - The responses to oxidative stress induced by diabetes may be change in the brain, liver and muscle. Moderate physical exercise with vitamins C and E (VCE) supplementation can be beneficial to diabetes due to reducing free radical production in the tissues of diabetic pregnant rats. The author investigated the effect of VCE supplementation and physical moderate exercise on lipid peroxidation and antioxidant levels in the muscle, liver and brain of STZ- induced diabetic pregnant rats.

Fifty female Wistar rats were used and were randomly divided into five groups. First and second were used as the control and pregnant control group. Third group was the pregnant diabetic group. The fourth group was the diabetic-pregnant-exercise group. VCE- supplemented feed was given to pregnant-diabetic-exercise rats constituting the fifth group. Animals in the exercised groups were moderately exercised daily on a treadmill (16.1 m/min, 45 min/d) for three weeks (five days a week). Diabetes was induced on day zero of the study before mating animals. Muscle, liver and brain samples were taken from all animals on day 20.

Exercise and administration of VCE to pregnant diabetic rats resulted in significant decrease in the glutathione peroxidase (GSH-Px), reduced glutathione (GSH), vitamin E and β- carotene levels and the elevated lipid peroxidation levels. The values in the muscle were most affected by diabetes. Exercise in the diabetic pregnant group did not change GSH and vitamin E levels in the brain although lipid peroxidation levels in the liver, muscle and brain decreased. In the diabetic pregnant animals, the decreased □- carotene, vitamins A and E concentration and GSH and GSH-Px levels in muscle and liver did not improve through exercise only although their concentrations were increased by VCE supplementation.

In conclusion, the authors results suggest that responses of the brain to oxidative stress by diabetes are quite different from those in liver and muscle. There was the beneficial effect of exercise with a dietary VCE on investigated antioxidant defenses and tissue lipid peroxidation in the muscle and liver of the diabetic- pregnant rat model. The moderate exercise training with a VCE supplementation may play a role in preventing diabetic muscle and liver diseases of diabetic pregnant animals.

In: Exercise and Health Research
Editor: M. D. Johansen, pp. 1-35

ISBN: 978-1-60021-985-6
© 2008 Nova Science Publishers, Inc.

Chapter 1

THE INFLUENCE OF BODY WEIGHT AND SHAPE IN DETERMINING FEMALE AND MALE PHYSICAL ATTRACTIVENESS

*Viren Swami**

Department of Psychology, University College London,
London, UK

ABSTRACT

Evolutionary psychologists have argued that there exist universally shared criteria of attractiveness, which are potent cues to a person's potential reproductive success. This article reviews the current state of evolutionary psychology's study of female and male physical attractiveness. The former focuses on body shape as measured by the waist-to-hip ratio (WHR) and body weight scaled for height, or the body mass index (BMI), whereas the latter examines the waist-to-chest ratio (WCR). The evidence seems to point to BMI being the dominant cue for female physical attractiveness, with WHR playing a more minor role. The opposite is true for male attractiveness, with WCR playing a more important role than either the WHR or BMI. Importantly, cross-cultural studies have suggested that there are significant differences for physical attractiveness in terms of body shape and weight,

---

* Address for correspondence: Viren Swami, Department of Psychology, University College London, 26, Bedford Way, London WC1E 6BT. Email: viren.swami@ucl.ac.uk.

which evolutionary psychological arguments have difficulty in explaining. Alternative explanations and the future of the field are discussed in conclusion.

Keywords: Evolutionary psychology, physical attractiveness, waist-to-hip ratio, body mass index, waist-to-chest ratio.

INTRODUCTION

Although human beauty has been a topic of debate for poets, philosophers and scientists for centuries, most lay theories of physical attractiveness concur with David Hume's (1757: 208-209) declaration that beauty 'is no quality in things themselves; it exists merely in the mind that contemplates them; and each mind perceives a different beauty.' Recently, however, investigators have claimed that progress in theories of evolutionary psychology and empirical evidence has challenged this conclusion (Buss, 1994, 1999; Buss, and Schmitt, 1993; Symons, 1995). Evolutionary psychologists argue that there exist universally shared criteria of attractiveness, which are potent cues to a person's potential reproductive success. Within this tradition, males and females are said to select partners that will enhance their reproductive success, and there has been a concurrent emphasis on the attractiveness of salient morphological features. The latter are said to honestly signal that one individual is more 'desirable' than another (Buss, 1994, 1999).

Much of the literature within this field has concerned two potentially critical cues in women, namely, body shape and weight scaled for height, or the body mass index (BMI). This chapter begins by reviewing the evidence in support of the thesis that female body *shape* is an important predictor of physical attractiveness, before examining comparable evidence in favour of body *weight*. In addition, some recent studies have begun to look at male physical attractiveness from an evolutionary perspective. This chapter considers evidence in this regard, before finally presenting alternative (but not mutually exclusive) explanations for these findings, and suggests directions for future research.

THE WAIST-TO-HIP RATIO IN WOMEN

Overall body weight is the most noticeable change caused by pubertal onset in women, and the traditional technique for estimating body weight has been the BMI. However, in a series of papers published in the 1990s, Singh (1993a, 1993b, 1994a, 1994b, 1994c, 1994d, 1995a, 1995b; Singh, and Luis, 1995; Singh, and Young, 1995) argued that the increase in BMI observed in women during puberty does not take into account the sex-dependent anatomical distribution of fat deposits. Instead, he made the point that the deposit and utilisation of fat from various anatomical areas is regulated by sex hormones. Oestrogen inhibits fat deposit in the abdominal region and maximally stimulates fat deposit in the gluteofemoral region (buttocks and thighs) more than in any other region of the body. Testosterone, on the other hand, stimulates fat deposit in the abdominal region and inhibits deposits in the gluteofemoral region (Björntorp, 1997). It is this sexually dimorphic body fat distribution that primarily sculpts typical body shape differences between the sexes that become noticeable after pubertal onset.

Before puberty, body shape is more or less similar for both males and females (Pond, 1978). After puberty, however, women have greater amounts of body fat (adipose tissue) in the lower part of the body, thus engendering what is known as gynoid fat distribution, whereas men have greater amounts of fat in the upper body, or what is known as android fat distribution (Björntorp, 1987, 1991; Rebuffé-Scrive, 1988, 1991). This sexually dimorphic fat distribution is most commonly quantified by measuring the ratio of the circumference of the waist (the narrowest portion below the ribs and above the iliac crest) to the circumference of the hips (at the level of the greatest protrusion of the buttocks), that is, the waist-to-hip ratio (WHR).

These differences between the gynoid and the android fat distribution engender a noticeable and typical sex difference (Molarius, Seidell, Sans, Tuomilehto, and Kuulasmaa, 1999). For healthy, pre-menopausal Caucasian women, the range of WHRs has been shown to be between 0.67 and 0.80 (Lanska, Lanska, Hartz, and Rimm, 1985); for healthy Caucasian men, it ranges from 0.85 to 0.95 (Jones, Hunt, Brown, and Norgan, 1986; Marti, et al., 1991). Women typically maintain a lower WHR than men through adulthood, although the WHR approaches the masculine range after menopause (Arechiga, Prado, Canto, and Carmenati, 2001; Kirschner, and Samojlik, 1991). It has been shown that the increase in WHR in menopausal women is caused by the reduction in oestrogen levels.

This interpretation seems to be corroborated by the observation that pre-menopausal women suffering from polycystic ovary syndrome (which is marked by impaired oestrogen production) have higher WHRs than age-matched non-patients (Pasquali, *et al.*, 1999; Pirwany, *et al.*, 2001). Additionally, Pasquali, *et al.* (1999) have shown that when women suffering from polycystic ovary syndrome are administered an oestrogen-progestagen compound, their WHRs become lower over time. Conversely, men suffering from disorders associated with endocrine imbalance (for example, Klinefelter syndrome) or treated with oestrogen for testosterone-dependent cancer of the prostate, develop gynoid fat distribution and lower WHRs that are more typical or normal-weight women (Kirschner, and Samojlik, 1991).

Singh also pointed out that risk for various diseases depends not only on the degree of obesity as measured by BMI, but importantly on anatomical location of fat deposits (Guo, Salisbury, Roche, Chumela, and Siervogel, 1994; Kissebah, and Krakower, 1994), that is, that the WHR is systematically related to a variety of life outcomes. In particular, WHR is a risk factor for cardiovascular disorders, adult-onset diabetes, hypertension, endometrial, ovarian and breast cancer, and gall bladder disease (Folsom, *et al.*, 1993; Huang, Willet, and Colditz, 1999; Misra, and Vikram, 2003). In addition, the WHR signals all the conditions that affect women's reproductive status. Females with higher WHRs have more irregular menstrual cycles (van Hooff, *et al.*, 2000), and WHR becomes significantly lower during ovulation compared to non-ovulatory phases of the menstrual cycle (Singh, Davis, and Randall, 2000). The probability of successful pregnancy induction is also affected by WHR – women participating in donor insemination programmes have a lower probability of conception if their WHR is greater than 0.8, after controlling for age, BMI and parity (Zaadstra, *et al.*, 1993). Married women with a higher WHR and a lower BMI also have more difficulty becoming pregnant and have their first live birth at a later age than married women with lower WHR (Kaye, Folsom, Prineas, and Gapstur, 1990). It has been suggested that the lower pregnancy rate in women with high WHRs, compared to women with low WHRs, may have to do with a problem in embryo development and its viability (Waas, Waldenstrom, Rossner, and Hellberg, 1997).

THE IDEAL WAIST-TO-HIP RATIO

According to Singh, one of the main problems facing our hunter-gatherer ancestors during human evolutionary history was the identification of mate value. To overcome this problem, he argues that males possess 'perceptual mechanisms' to detect and use information conveyed by the WHR in determining a woman's attractiveness as a potential mate. Because of this, it is possible to systematically change men's evaluations of women's attractiveness by manipulating the size of the WHR alone. In support of this idea, Singh amassed evidence for an evolved male preference for a WHR of 0.7, which correspond closely to the optimal in terms of health and fertility.

To begin with, Singh (1993a, 1993b) developed a set of twelve two-dimensional, line drawings of the female figure, which were systematically varied with respect to overall body weight (underweight, normal weight, and overweight) and the WHR. Within each weight category, line drawings represented four levels of the WHR by changing the waist size. In a series of experiments using these drawings, Singh (1993a, 1993b, 1994c; Singh, and Luis, 1995) described a negative correlation between WHR and female attractiveness, with line drawings with gynoid WHRs (0.7 and 0.8) being judged as the most attractive. However, the relationship is not strictly monotone – beyond a certain point, an extremely low WHR may appear grotesque and repelling (Furnham, and Radley, 1989).

The finding that normal weight female figures with a low WHR are judged as most attractive has been replicated with participants in the United States, United Kingdom, Germany and Australia using the twelve line drawings developed from the initial study (Connally, Slaughter, and Mealy, submitted; Furnham, Tan, and McManus, 1997; Henss, 1995, 2000; Singh, 1994c). For Singh (1993a: 304), the WHR 'acts as a wide first-pass filter, which would automatically exclude women who are unhealthy or who have low reproductive capacity.' It is only after this 'culturally invariant' filter is passed that other features such as the face, skin or weight (which may vary between cultures) become utilised in final mate selection.

A BROKEN FILTER?

Reviewing the literature suggests that the evidence may once have supported Singh's conclusions, but that it may not anymore. For one thing, several authors have questioned the validity of Singh's findings based on the use of evidence purporting to show that the WHR 0.7 is optimal for health and reproductive potential. For example, Singh (2002) cites evidence that fat deposits in early pregnancy are primarily localised in the pelvic girdle regions, and hence, an increase in WHR in the absence of any significant weight gain is one of the first signs of pregnancy. Coupled with this is the finding that reproductive history such as parity or lactation can also increase the size of a woman's WHR (Tonkelaar, *et al.*, 1990). Singh uses such data to support his claim that the WHR provides reliable information about mate nulliparousity and female pregnancy induced by other males during human evolutionary history. But he does not present evidence to suggest that nulliparousity and mate pregnancy were important problems for human ancestral populations – the lack of detailed information about hunter-gatherer populations in our evolutionary past precludes any such conjecture. Importantly, Wetsman (1998) reports that obesity is typically presumed to have been more rare in our evolutionary past, especially among reproductive-aged women. If correct, then the consequences of different kinds of obesity could not have been a target of selection.

On the other hand, from a methodological point of view, Tassinary and Hansen (1998) have criticised the fact that research in this area has been almost exclusively restricted to the set of line drawings developed by Singh. They argued that the use of line drawings to depict variations in WHR used by Singh and other researchers lacked ecological validity. As Singh self-critically indicates, line-drawing stimuli are often impoverished and unrealistic, relying on a single original image from which modifications are made. It is thus ecologically unrealistic to show modified versions of the same stimulus and expect each to be rated on its own merits, without any recourse to a comparison with variations that have been presented simultaneously or sequentially.

To examine the issue, Tassinary and Hansen (1998) developed a set of their own line drawings comprising twenty-seven female figures that varied in weight (light, moderate, heavy), waist size (small, medium, large) and hip size (small, medium, large). With this new set of images, the authors found the weight of the figure to be a more potent factor than the WHR. Light- and moderate-weight figures were judged to be much more attractive than the heavy figures, whereas moderate-weight and heavy figures were judged to be much more fecund than the light figures. They thus suggest that the apparent positive association between the WHR, judged attractiveness and judged fecundity is an artefact of a limited stimulus set, and argue that their findings 'demonstrate that weight and hip size are important and independent co-determinants of both relative attractiveness and fecundity, and that the WHR is of marginal importance for predicting relative attractiveness. This pattern of results... constitutes a clear and unambiguous disconfirmation of the WHR hypothesis' (Tassinary, and Hansen, 1998: 154-155). More recently, however, Streeter and McBurney (2003), using stimuli that statistically controlled for body weight, failed to replicate the positive relationship between WHR and attractiveness reported by Tassinary and Hansen.

A number of other studies have also attempted to overcome the ecological invalidity associated with line drawings. Henss (2000), for example, designed a study using full frontal photographs that included the face and breasts of different women with computer-altered WHR. For each photograph, two versions of the WHR were created using morphing techniques – in one picture the waist was tightened (lower WHR), and in the other it was widened (higher WHR). Using this new set of stimuli, Henss found support for Singh's contention that the WHR is an essential attribute of the attractiveness of the female figure. However, Henss also pointed out that when whenever both WHR and overall body weight have been manipulated, it is evident that weight accounts for more variance than WHR. All the evidence, he concludes, underlines the fact that the WHR plays a less potent role than the weight category or the face.

This is also the conclusion of Forestell, Humphrey and Stewart (2004), who used Tassinary and Hansen's line drawings to test the degree to which various body shape characteristics influence women's ratings of attractiveness of female figures. Their results showed that participants preferred figures that had WHRs around 0.7, but that as body size increased, larger WHRs tended to be preferred. Figures with small and medium waists and hips were generally preferred regardless of body weight, but figures with large hips were preferred less regardless of other shape characteristics. In addition, when photographs of women with WHR manipulated either by hip or waist changes are used, attractiveness seems to be more influenced by changes in waist than hip size (Rozmus-Wrzesinska, and Pawlowski, 2005). It seems likely, therefore, that body weight, waist size and hip size all interact to influence women's ratings of attractiveness of other female figures (Furnham, Petrides, and Constantinides, 2005).

FEMALE BODY WEIGHT

Tovée and his colleagues (Tovée, Maisey, Emery, and Cornelissen, 1999; Tovée, Mason, Emery, McClusky, and Cohen-Tovée, 1997; Tovée, Reinhardt, Emery and Cornelissen, 1998) have objected to the extant WHR research on the grounds that none of the previous studies used women with known WHRs. Thus, it may very well be that such a relationship does not generalise to an actual population. In addition, they argue that the assumption held by WHR researchers that the BMI of figures is held constant when narrowing the waist is false (Tovée, and Cornelissen, 2001). When the figures are modified by a altering the width of the torso around the waist, this not only alters the WHR, but also apparent BMI. As the value of the WHR rises, so does that of the apparent BMI, and so it is not possible to say whether changes in attractiveness ratings are made on the basis of WHR or BMI, or both (Tovée, and Cornelissen, 1999; Tovée, et al., 1999). This error is intrinsic to most studies that have used line drawings, including the study by Tassinary and Hansen (1998), but is also duplicated by Henss (2000). In short,

Tovée *et al.* (1999) suggest that the importance attributed to WHR in previous studies is likely to be an artefact of co-varying WHR with apparent BMI.

To investigate the relative importance of BMI and WHR in the perception of female attractiveness, Tovée and his colleagues used images of real women in a standard pose and distance from view. By using images of real women (as opposed to line drawings) both BMI and actual WHR were known precisely and their effects could be estimated separately. A further advantage of these stimuli was the fact that the heads of the women were obscured, so that facial attractiveness would not be a factor in participants' ratings. Multiple regressions of the attractiveness ratings for these images of real women suggests that although both shape and body mass are significant predictors of female attractiveness, weight scaled for height is a far more important factor than WHR (Tovée *et al.*, 1998, 1999; Tovée, and Cornelissen, 2001). BMI is said to account for more than 70 per cent of the variance in their analyses, whereas WHR accounts for little more than 2 per cent. These results also hold when the women are presented in profile, as opposed to a frontal view (Tovée, and Cornelissen, 2001), when computer-generated photographic stimuli are used in a between-subjects design (Puhl, and Boland, 2001) and when three-dimensional images are used (Fan, Liu, Wu, and Dai, 2004).

However, the multivariate analyses by Tovée and his colleagues used the widest range of BMI and WHR values available. One objection to this is that the relative ranges of BMI and WHR are unequal, and that the apparent importance of BMI in such studies is due to greater relative variation in this parameter than in WHR (Singh, 2002). To address this problem, Tovée, Hancock, Mahmoodi, Singleton, and Cornelissen (2002) used images of female bodies where the range of BMI values was strictly controlled (thereby giving WHR an 'advantage'), but WHR still failed to emerge as a strong determinant for attractiveness. In a second experiment, the researchers disturbed the natural relationship between the WHR and BMI. Normally, BMI and WHR tend to be positively correlated in the female population, that is, women with a higher BMI tend to have a less curvaceous shape. Instead, Tovée *et al.* (2002) deliberately chose a set of photographic images that demonstrated an inverse correlation between BMI and WHR, that is, a group in which as the women become heavier, they also become more curvaceous. Even though the relative ranges of WHR and BMI should favour WHR in this sample of images, BMI again emerged as the dominant predictor. In other words, women with a low BMI and a high WHR were judged as more attractive, rather than women with a high BMI and a low WHR.

The finding that BMI may be the primary determinant of female attractiveness is consistent with the fact that successful female fashion and glamour models all fall within a narrow BMI range (Tovée, *et al.*, 1997), albeit an underweight range. From an evolutionary psychological point of view, Tovée and his colleagues suggest that there are advantages to using BMI as a basis for mate selection, as BMI provides a reliable cue to female health (Manson, *et al.*, 1995; Willet, *et al.*, 1995) and reproductive potential (Frisch, 1988; Lake, Power, and Cole, 1997; Reid, and van Vugt, 1987; Wang, Davies and Norman, 2000). Put together, Tovée and his colleagues suggest that the balance between the optimal BMI for health and fertility is struck at around a value of 19kg/m², which, in their studies, is also the preferred BMI for attractiveness. In addition, Tovée, *et al.* (2002) suggest that actual WHR may be limited in its utility. For example, there is a considerable overlap in the WHRs of populations of normal women and anorexic patients (Tovée, *et al.*, 1997). The latter group are amenorrhoeic, and so a woman with an effective fertility of zero can have the same WHR as a woman with normal fertility.

Based on these findings, Tovée *et al.* (2002) have suggested that one simply does not need to be very sensitive to shape cues. In a normal situation, BMI and body shape are linked, which would suggest that, on average, a body with a particular BMI would tend to have a particular shape. An alternative explanation is that there exists a 'hierarchy of cues' used in partner selection. Features such as WHR may be used to discriminate broad categories, such as male from female or pregnant from non-pregnant. Discriminating within the category of potential partners, one may use such cues as BMI and then other cues such as the proportions of the body to discriminate between women of very similar BMI.

FEMALE ATTRACTIVENESS ACROSS CULTURES

Preferences for a low WHR have been replicated in a wide range of countries, including Australia, the UK, Germany, Greece, India and the Azores (Connally, *et al.*, submitted; Furnham, Dias, and McClelland, 1998; Furnham, Lavancy, and McClelland, 2001; Furnham, Moutafi, and Baguma, 2002; Furnham, Tan, and McManus, 1997; Singh, 2000, 2004, 2004; Singh, and Luis, 1995). This has been taken as evidence for the universal and culturally invariant nature of WHR as a signal for mate selection. However, a single factor shared by all these studies, which makes the claim unwarranted, is that they were carried out in industrial societies. What is clear from the literature is that cultures differ widely in their attitudes towards such things as obesity and body shape (Brown, and Konner, 1987; Ford, and Beach, 1952; Sobal, and Stunkard, 1989).

In an early cross-cultural study, Furnham and Alibhai (1983) compared Black Kenyan to White British and British Kenyan participants' ratings of line figures from anorexic to obese, reporting that Black Kenyan participants viewed obese female shapes more positively than either British or British Kenyan participants, both of which were indistinguishably negative in their evaluation. Replication in Uganda also found the native African sample to be much more approving of obese female figures than a British comparison group (Furnham, and Baguma, 1994).

Ethnographers have also noted the greater positive association between body fat and prestige in the South Pacific, as body fat is more likely to reflect access to food resources (Brewis, and McGarvey, 2000; Craig, Swinburn, Matenga-Smith, Matangi, and Vaughan 1996; Wilkinson, Ben-Tovin, and Walker, 1994). Becker (1995), for example, reported that Fijian men and women were more tolerant of overweight and obese line drawings than a British comparison. This line of evidence is corroborated by a raft of studies (for example, Akan, and Greilo, 1995; Perez, and Joiner, 2003; Poran, 2002; Rucker, and Cash, 1992) and reviews of the literature (Crago, Shisslak, and Estes, 1996; Fitzgibbon, *et al.*, 1998) demonstrating that African Americans have different attitudes about weight, body shape, and attractiveness than Caucasians, with overall less drive for thinness and greater acceptance of larger body proportions.

The argument remains, however, that while preferences for body weight may differ across cultures, preferences for a low WHR do not. What is the evidence for this? Wetsman and Marlowe (1999) elicited WHR preferences from a hunter-gatherer tribe called the Hadza, in Tanzania, who subsist almost exclusively from foraging wild foods. They found that the size of WHR does not affect judgements of attractiveness. Instead, the Hadza preferred heavy to medium and medium to lightweight line drawings when selecting for attractiveness, health and desirability as a wife, regardless of WHR. The authors concluded that the WHR may be more akin to a 'second-pass filter': 'The first-pass filter could consist of partner preferences based on body weight... The influence of WHR may only become relevant when food resources are plentiful enough that the risk of starvation during pregnancy and lactation for women is minimal...' (Wetsman, and Marlowe, 1999: 226).

These results are strikingly similar to that of a previous study conducted amongst a relatively isolated population, the Matsiengka of southern Peru, who practise swidden (slash and burn) agriculture (Yu, and Shepard, 1998). The researchers tested three groups of the same population, differing in their degree of contact (and, therefore, their degree of 'westernisation'). The least westernised group, like the Hadza, ranked figures first by weight (high preferred to low) and then high WHR over low WHR, once again diametrically opposing findings using participants in industrial societies. The second, moderately westernised group differed in that they rated low WHR females as being more attractive and more desirable as spouses, but not more healthy. The third and most westernised group (first contacted 20 to 30 years previously) did not differ from male participants in the United States.

Marlowe and Wetsman (2001) recently returned to Tanzania with a new set of line drawings in which only the WHR was varied. With no weight variation, Hadza men preferred high WHRs, which the authors argue is nevertheless an artefact of the preference for heavier women. They argue that their (as well as Yu and Shepard's) findings can be explained by the fact that exposure to western media is likely to co-vary with dependence on wild versus domesticated foods. That is, the more subsistence-oriented a society is, and the more energetically expensive women's work, the more men will find heavier women attractive. Among foragers, women who are too thin and energetically stressed reach menarche later, ovulate less regularly, and have less capacity to support pregnancy and lactation (Ellison, 1990; Frisch, 1987). They argue that obesity does not exist among the Hadza and probably rarely, if ever, existed prior to agriculture. In the past, therefore, men should have been selected to find heavier women attractive, as indeed they do in many societies. Agriculture led to a more predictable, surplus food supply, the risk of obesity decreased, and men began to prefer low body mass indices. Thus, the more food-rich a society, and the longer it has been food-rich, the more likely a low WHR will be preferred. However, in a stratified society, a low preference might begin among upper strata men and spread to lower strata men, even if lower strata women are too poor to be at risk of obesity.

Furnham, Moutafi and Baguma (2002) have investigated the effect of weight and WHR on attractiveness ratings on subjects from Uganda, Greece and Britain. They too found a clear cultural influence on body size and shape preference – although the European data showed an overall preference for the 0.7 WHR, the Ugandan subjects gave the ratio of 0.5 the highest rating. A monotonic negative relationship between WHR and perceived attractiveness has in fact been proposed by researchers (Singh, 1993a), but using 0.7 as the lowest ratio. An extrapolation of this relationship would yield 0.5 as the most attractive WHR, but the evolutionary psychological hypothesis would also require it to be the most fertile and healthy ratio as well, which is not what has been reported. A possible explanation for the preference of the Ugandan subjects for the 0.5 ratio is that the 0.5 ratio could only be achieved by having a small waist and large hips, and large hips yield the impression of a heavier figure. Therefore, the preference of a 0.5 ratio could be explained by their preference for large figures, which can be seen by looking at the effect of weight on attractiveness ratings. Furnham, *et al.* (2002) hypothesised that they would find a preference of heavy figures by the Ugandans, in contrast to a preference of light figures by Greeks and the British. The results supported the hypothesis, suggesting that weight matters, sometimes over and above WHR.

This set of results is similar to that reported by Freedman, Carter, Sbrocco, and Gray (2004), who examined ethnic differences in male preferences for ideal body size and shape in women. The researchers found that African American men were more likely to choose heavier figures as ideal than Caucasian men did. Specifically, African American men disliked a low body weight for women more frequently than did their Caucasian counterparts. In addition, both ethnic groups chose figures with a low WHR, but African American men were more likely to choose a very low WHR as ideal. For the authors, the findings emphasized the importance of assessing male preferences for female shape (or WHR), but also showed weight to be a more important cue than WHR in the male selection process. It appears that African American men are more willing to idealise a woman of a heavier body size, with more curves, than do their Caucasian counterparts, and such differences may play a role in the differential messages that get communicated to women about the kinds of bodies that men like.

EXPLAINING CROSS-CULTURAL DIFFERENCES

An early attempt by evolutionary psychologists to explain cross-cultural differences in preferences for WHR rests on WHR acting as a predictor of child gender. A high pre-conceptual WHR is a good predictor of male offspring, and so in cultures that value male children, an androgynous body shape should be judged as more attractive. The predictive value of WHR is based on studies measuring women who already have children and correlating their WHR with the proportion of existing male offspring. Thus, two independent studies (Manning, Anderton, and Washington, 1996; Singh, and Zambarano, 1997) argued that women with high WHRs and thick waists tended to have more sons, and that preference for women with a high WHR might result in selection for increased testosterone levels in children. Similarly, Manning, Trivers, Singh and Thornhill (1999) presented data from a rural Jamaican population which showed that there is a positive association between a woman's waist circumference and her number of sons.

However, this model fails to explain why westernised indigenous populations in South America, for example, should prefer hour-glass-shaped women (Yu, and

Shepard, 1999). If it is argued that most traditional societies value strength (or sons), then South America's male-dominated economy should increase, not decrease, the value of males in westernised populations, and, by extension, the value of high WHR females. Yu and Shepard (1999) also argue that such preference changes as suggested by the adaptationist paradigm could not feasibly occur in a single generation from an evolutionary point of view. In addition, carrying a male child may alter the WHR in a different way to carrying a female child, and a high WHR may be an *effect* rather than a cause of offspring. To test the predictive power of pre-conceptual WHR and offspring gender, Tovée, Brown and Jacobs (2001) took WHR measures from 458 women who intended to become pregnant and then correlated with the gender of the subsequent child. Going against the grain of the thesis that WHR acts as a predictor of child gender, they found no significant correlation.

A different explanation for cross-cultural variation in preferences for WHR, but one that nevertheless remains compatible with evolutionary psychology, has been proposed by Sugiyama (2004). He argues that cross-cultural tests of the low-WHR hypothesis have used stimuli that were not scaled to local conditions: forager women have high fecundity, parasite loads and caloric dependence on fibrous foods, all of which increase WHR. Since mate selection should calibrate for local conditions, he argues that WHR-preference mechanisms will assess the local distribution of female WHR in relation to other correlates of mate value, and will recalibrate as conditions change. Instead of expecting uniform cross-cultural preference for a specific WHR value, researchers should anticipate only that values lower than the local average will be attractive, and that the influence of this factor relative to others will vary cross-culturally.

Taking into account the local distribution of Ecuadorian Shiwiar WHR, Sugiyama (2004) found that Shiwiar males use female WHR in a way that is consistent with the hypothesis that WHR assessment is sensitively calibrated to local parameters. When differences in body weight are minimised, Shiwiar men preferred lower-than-locally-average female WHR. However, the reliability of this study should be questioned: preferences were only elicited from 18 participants, and the stimuli did not completely unconfound body weight and WHR (Shiwiar men prefer higher-body-fat females within locally observed levels). Thus, when WHR and body fat were not independently assessed, Shiwiar men preferred high-WHR figures because they appear to weigh the most among the high-weight figures.

A different evolutionary argument suggests that the reported difference in preferences for WHR in different cultures may instead be based on BMI. Combined with the argument that WHR and body weight are confounded in line drawings, Tovée, and Cornelissen (2001) suggest that the same ideal BMI should not be expected for all racial groups and environments. On the basis of epidemiological evidence that suggests that different ethnic populations may have differing levels of risk for negative health consequences with changing BMI (for example, Kopelman, 2000; McKeigue, Shah, and Marmot, 1991; Shetty, and James, 1994), they suggest that there may be a different optimal BMI for health and longevity in different racial groups. As a consequence, there will be a preferred optimal BMI for each group, which will balance environmental and health factors, but that this optimal BMI may differ between groups and environments (Tovée, and Cornelissen, 2001).

Recently, Swami and his colleagues (for example, Swami, and Tovée, 2005a; Swami, Caprario, *et al.*, in press; Swami, Knight, *et al.*, submitted; Swami, Tovée, *et al.*, submitted) have tested this hypothesis in a series of cross-cultural replications of the BMI research. Swami and Tovée (2005a), for example, examined preferences for female physical attractiveness along a socio-economic gradient in Britain and Malaysia, from rural to semi-urban to urban. Their results showed that, regardless of the cultural setting, BMI was the primary predictor of attractiveness ratings, whereas WHR failed to emerge as a strong predictor. The authors also found that preferences for physical attractiveness varied with socio-economic setting, with rural observers preferring larger figures than semi-urban observers, who in turn preferred larger figures than urban observers.

Importantly, this study also examined the physical attractiveness preferences of observer groups of different racial origin from the same environment (Malay, Chinese and Indian in Kuala Lumpur). Studies have indicated that ethnic Malays, Chinese and Indians in South East Asia have different optimal BMIs for risk factors for morbidity and mortality (e.g., Deurenberg, Deurenberg-Yap, and Guricci, 2002), which would suggest that these ethnic groups should have different preferences for body weight. However, this was not the case: Malays, Chinese and Indians in Kuala Lumpur all had a similar preference for slender figures. Elsewhere, Swami, Tovée, *et al.* (submitted) have reported that physical attractiveness preferences can be modified, as attested by the changing preferences of migrants.

All the evidence, therefore, seems to point to body weight, rather than shape, acting as the primary predictor of female physical attractiveness. However, preferences for BMI appear to vary considerably depending on the socio-economic status of observers and, to a lesser degree, the cultural context occupied by observers. If this is true of female physical attractiveness, what of male attractive?

MALE PHYSICAL ATTRACTIVENESS

Although much research concerning physical attractiveness has focussed on the female body, researchers are increasingly paying attention to masculinity and the male body (for example, Stam, 1998). What little work has been done employs an evolutionary psychological perspective and considers different traits to be an indicator of genetic variability. This explanation assumes that a reliable connection exists between body attractiveness and male quality; that male attractiveness is an indicator or some component of fitness such as health and vigour; and that females detect and use this indicator for choosing a mate (Shackelford, et al., 2000)

The most obvious case of sexually selected characters in humans concerns features such as beards and body shape that differ conspicuously between the sexes (Barber, 1995). Thus, it has been argued that men with dominance- and masculinity-related facial and body characteristics are considered most physically and sexually attractive. Testosterone and areas of the body indexing testosterone play key roles, as dominant males have higher testosterone levels (Ehrenkantz, Bliss, and Sheard, 1974). It has also been suggested that aspects of male body build, particularly the upper torso, might be sexually selected. The shoulders of men, their upper body musculature and biceps are all more developed than in women, even when differences in stature are accounted for (Ross, and Ward, 1982), and these characteristics are influenced by testosterone levels (Björntorp, 1987).

Using silhouettes as stimuli, a number of studies have shown that females tend to prefer a moderately developed male torso than extremely muscular physiques (Barber, 1995). However, most of these studies have not looked explicitly at male bodily physique, focussing rather on the waist-to-hip ratio (WHR; the ratio of the circumference of the waist to the circumference of the hips). According to Singh (1995), men with WHRs in the 'desirable' range (0.90 to 0.95) should have fared better when competing for mates in evolutionary history. To test this idea, Singh (1995) had participants rate line drawings depicting men with different WHRs and body sizes. Men with WHRs near the desirable range were consistently rated as the healthiest and most attractive mates. They were also rated as being more intelligent and having better leadership qualities. In contrast, men with WHRs lower than 0.90 or higher than 0.95 were rated as less healthy, less attractive and as having less-desirable personality characteristics. This basic pattern of results has been replicated by a number of different researchers (Furnham, et al., 1997; Henss, 1995; Lynch, and Zellner, 1999; Olivardia, et al., 2004).

However, more recent research using photographic stimuli shows that while the WHR, body mass index (BMI) and waist-to-chest ratio (WCR) are all significant contributors to male attractiveness, WCR was the principal determinant and accounted for 56 per cent of the variance (Maisey, Vale, Cornelissen, and Tovée, 1999; see also Fan, Dai, Liu, and Wu, 2005). By contrast, BMI accounted for only 12.7 per cent of the variance and the WHR was not a significant predictor of attractiveness. Maisey, *et al.* (1999) concluded that women's ratings of male attractiveness can be explained by simple physical characteristics that measure body shape (in particular the WCR). Women are said to prefer men whose torso has an 'inverted triangle' shape, that is, a narrow waist and a broad chest and shoulders, which is consistent with physical strength and muscle development in the upper body (for example, Franzoi, and Herzog, 1987; Horvath, 1979). This finding is comparable with other studies using line drawings which show that women prefer men with a 'V-shape' (wider shoulders than chest, which was again is wider than the hips; Frederick, and Haselton, 2003; Furnham, and Radley, 1989; Hughes, and Gallup, 2003; Lavrakas, 1975).

MALE ATTRACTIVENESS ACROSS CULTURES

If judgements of attractiveness are an innate preference, as evolutionary psychology argues, then it might be suggested that these preferences should be consistent across cultures. Although there is now a growing body of evidence examining body type preferences for the male body, the literature examining these preferences cross-culturally remains limited. Using an undergraduate sample of Caucasian and Asian-American students, Mintz and Kashubeck (1999) found that males aspired for a large, muscular cultural ideal that does not differ between ethnic groups. However, while Mintz and Kashubeck (1999) explored satisfaction with specific body parts, they did not specifically investigate the interaction between ethnicity and gender on overall body figure preference. A more recent study suggests that Asian-American men are more invested in developing a large, muscular body (Barnett, Keel, and Conoscenti, 2001), but to date few studies have examined male physical attractiveness cross-nationally.

One exception to this is a recent study by Swami and Tovée (2005b), which examined preferences for male physical attractiveness in Britain and Malaysia. The results of their study show that a woman's rating of male bodily attractiveness can be explained by simple physical characteristics, in particular the WCR and BMI. However, there are clear cross-cultural differences in the way these characteristics are used. In *urban* settings in Malaysia and Britain, the WCR is the primary component of attractiveness ratings, suggesting that body shape is more important for male attractiveness than body size. Women prefer men whose torso has an 'inverted triangle' shape, but the BMI of the male body is comparatively unimportant. This is distinguishable from investigations of female attractiveness, which show that body weight is the primary predictor of attractiveness ratings (Fan, *et al.*, 2004; Tovée, *et al.*, 1999).

By contrast, BMI is the primary cue for male attractiveness in *rural* Malaysia, with body shape (as measured by the WCR and WHR) playing comparatively minor roles. The preference among rural participants for heavier men is combined with a preference for a more tubular body shape (that is, changing body shape has less of an effect on attractiveness in the rural group, and a less curvaceous shape is regarded as relatively more attractive in the rural group than in the other observer groups). This set of findings is striking given existing cross-cultural evidence suggesting that Asian-American men, like their Caucasian counterparts, are invested in developing a large, muscular body (Barnett, *et al.*, 2001; Mintz, and Kashubeck, 1999). Rather, when ratings are elicited from rural contexts, body size and not shape is the primary cue for male physical attractiveness.

SOCIOCULTURAL THEORY

The results of recent studies examining male and female physical attractiveness across cultures suggests that evolutionary explanations for these findings are problematic. Some evolutionary psychologists have attempted to provide a more rounded theory of attractiveness by combining evolutionary and social explanations of mate choice. (Swami, and Tovée, 2005a). Sociocultural theories have typically been shunned by evolutionary psychologists, but nevertheless provides substantial explanatory power for the findings of research regarding physical attractiveness.

Sociocultural theory emphasises the learning of preferences for body sizes in social and cultural contexts (Smolak, and Levine, 1996). With regard to the female body, the results of research within the Euro-American cultural sphere show that prejudice and discrimination against heavyweight people flourishes and remains largely legal and culturally approved (Crandall, 1994). Parental and peer influences have been implicated in the development of ideas concerning what constitutes an 'ideal' female image (for example, Gordon, 2000), but most researchers believe that the mass media plays a more significant role in influencing preferences for thin female figures in western societies by exhibiting underweight female models (for example, Bryant, and Zhilman, 2002; Harrison, 1997).

Research on Miss America contestants and *Playboy* centrefolds, for example, has shown that the ideal became increasingly thinner over a 20 period, between 1959 and 1978, while women actually became 4 per cent heavier (Garner, Garfinkel, Schwartz, and Thompson, 1980). A follow-up study found that this trend continued between 1979 and 1988: Miss America contestants continued to become thinner, whereas *Playboy* centrefolds fell into a plateau of very low BMIs (Wiseman, Gray, Mosimann, and Ahrens, 1992). Others have examined body satisfaction and eating disorder symptamology as correlates of using mass media (for example, Abramson, and Valene, 1991; Baker, Sivyer, and Towell, 1998; Cash, Cash, and Butters, 1983; Posavac, Posavac, and Weigel, 2001), the idea being that the mass media promulgates a slender ideal that elicits negative affect. Thus, the preference for relatively slender ideals in industrialised settings in the current study may be traced back to the emphasis on a slim physique and negative stereotyping of obese figures (Becker, and Hamburg, 1996).

While thin figures are typically regarded as 'ideal' in mainstream, western culture, cross-ethnic and cross-cultural research reveals differing perceptions of attractiveness and healthy body sizes (Miller, and Pumariega, 2001; Powers, 1980). In most traditional, non-western settings, body fat is believed to be an indicator of wealth and prosperity, with obesity as a symbol of economic success, femininity, and sexual capacity (Ghannam, 1997; Nasser, 1988; Rudovksy, 1974). In less affluent societies, there is often a positive relationship between increased socio-economic status and body weight. Only high-status individuals would have been able to put on body weight, which would explain why the majority of the world's cultures had or have ideals of feminine beauty that include plumpness (Anderson, Crawford, Nadeau, and Lindberg, 1992; Brown, and Konner, 1987), as it would have been advantageous for women to be able to store excess food as fat in times of surplus.

The findings reported by Swami and Tovée (2005a), therefore, lend credence to the view that physical attractiveness may be linked less to ethnicity than modernity or socio-economic status. Lee and Lee (2000: 324) have argued that economic liberalisation has encouraged the deregulation of mass media, which projects a powerful image that 'rigidly equates success with a young, slender and, glamorously adorned woman' (Lee, and Lee, 2000: 324). For Nasser (1994, 1997), the transculturality of body image disturbance is evidence of the globalisation of fat-phobia due to the emergence of a culturally shrunken world by a virtue of mass communication technology. Studies conducted in less developed countries show an increasing influence of western culture infused through technology, which have been shown to engender a desire on the part of adolescents, particularly women, to be thin (Wang, Popkin, and Thai, 1998).

Of course, it would be wrong to attribute preferences of physical attractiveness to 'westernisation' alone. Rather, the intensification of preferences for slim physiques is embedded in a 'gendered complex of hegemonic forces that accompany global economic change' (Lee, and Lee, 2000: 324). Rapid industrialisation and urbanisation have meant unparalleled changes in women's condition, with regards to education, employment opportunities, mate choice, birth control and legal rights. These changes have created conflicting demands on young women to strive simultaneously for career accomplishment while maintaining their physical attractiveness (Malson, 1998). Along with increasing affluence, there has also been an increase in the prevalence of worldwide obesity that legitimises the pursuit of thinness and a fear of fatness.

SOCIOCULTURAL THEORY AND THE MALE BODY

In opposition to evolutionary psychological explanations, it has been suggested that society has expectations for ideal male body shapes (Hesse-Biber, 1996; Murray, Touyz, and Beumont, 1996) and that males in urban contexts increasingly compare their bodies to idealised media and cultural images (Davis, and Katzman, 1997; Heinberg, Thompson, and Stormer, 1995; McCreary, and Sasse, 2000). Although gender differences emerge in attitudes toward cultural ideals of attractiveness, with women more motivated to conform to these ideals than men, sociocultural pressures concerning male body image seems to be on the increase. For example, one content analysis found a consistency in the V-shaped standard of male bodily attractiveness presented in US men's magazines between 1960 and 1992 (Petrie, et al., 1996). In a more recent study, Leit, Pope and Gray (2001) examined centrefold models in *Playgirl* from 1973 to 1997, and found that the cultural norm for the ideal male body has become increasingly muscular, especially in the 1990s.

Similarly, in studying the media's portrayal of the ideal body shape for men, Andersen and DiDomenico (1992) found that men's magazines published significantly more advertisements and articles about changing body shape than about losing weight, suggesting that men might be more concerned with overall physique than with body fat. Another study found that boys' action toys have become increasingly muscular over time, with many contemporary figures having physiques more muscular than is humanly attainable (Pope, Olivardia, Gruber, and Borowiecki, 1999). For Pope, Phillips and Olivardia (2000: 36), the contemporary muscular male ideal featured in the media represents a 'hypermale' or 'more male than male' look, characterised by a disproportionate amount of muscularity in the shoulders and upper arms.

The preference for a large, muscular, and mesomorphic body type in industrialised settings develops at a very young age (Staffieri, 1967), and reaches its peak during early adolescence and early adulthood (Collins, and Plahn, 1988; McCreary, and Sasse, 2000). Importantly, the development of such preferences has been linked with media use and exposure (Morry, and Staska, 2001). In a recent study, Botta (2003) surveyed US college students to test the extent to which reading fashion, sports, health or fitness magazines is related to body image and eating disorders. Results indicated that, for men specifically, reading was linked to increased muscularity, which means that the more time they spent reading, the more likely they were to engage in behaviours intended to increase muscle composition. Furthermore, the absence of a strong preference for muscular, V-shaped bodies among rural participants in the present study lends credence to the view that such an ideal is a culturally-influenced phenomenon.

However, it would be overly simplistic to blame media influences alone. Emerging evidence highlights other personal and sociocultural factors, especially parental and peer influences (Field, et al., 2001; Ricciardelli, and McCabe, 2001). For example, adolescent boys gain greater peer acceptance and popularity with both same-gender and other-gender peers by achieving a more muscular body (Eppright, Sanfancon, Beck, and Bradley, 1997; Silbereisen, and Kracker, 1997). Another possibility is that, in most industrialised settings, women have rapidly achieved parity with men in many aspects of life, leaving men with only their bodies as a distinguishing source of masculinity (Faludi, 1999; Leit, et al., 2001). Images of muscular, fit and toned men are argued to represent men seeking to embody the physical strength, hardness and power associated with the traditional muscular ideal, signalling distance from traditional cultural ideas about feminity. The contemporary preoccupation with abdominal stomach muscles has been discussed precisely in these terms by Baker (1997), who argues that this preoccupation is a way for men faced with decline in physical labour and increasing leisure time, and a related increase in girth, to hold on to the outward appearance of masculinity. If the softness and roundness of women's bodies are viewed as the apothesis of assumed femininity, then men's aspiration for abdominal tautness may be offering them a means to affirm a male-female difference. White and Gillet (1994) have, likewise, commented on the muscular body as an attempt at literally embodying traditional masculine ideals. They argue that the presentation of muscular masculinity as a cultural ideal may be a form of resistance to alternative masculinities that contest power hierarchies among men.

A WORKING HYPOTHESIS

The finding that preference for body weight and shape varies according to socio-economic status is in line with earlier ethnographic reports. Until recently, this pattern linking resource availability (as indicated by socio-economic status) and female body weight lacked an obvious psychological mechanism. Nelson and Morrison (2005), however, proposed an implicit psychological mechanism based on the situational influence of environmental conditions, which does not require the invoking of any evolved mechanism. They argue that collective resource scarcity has consequences for individual resources, as individual members of a society in which resources are scarce are likely to lack resources themselves. They further argue that the affective and physiological states associated with individual-level resource availability provide implicit information about collective resource availability, and that this information then plays a role in the construction of preferences.

In a series of studies, Nelson and Morrison (2005) tested this hypothesis by manipulating people's financial satisfaction or hunger (both these being proxies for personal resources in industrialised societies) and measuring their preferences for potential romantic partners. Their studies confirmed that financially dissatisfied and hungry men preferred a heavier mate than did financially satisfied men or satiated men respectively. Swami and Tovée (in press) have since confirmed the finding manipulating hunger using photographic stimuli, with hungrier men preferring larger figures than satiated men.

These studies provide evidence that *temporary affective states* can produce individual variation in mate preferences that mirrors patterns of cultural differences. In this sense, ratings of attractiveness vary over time. The mood or state of the rater can subtly but significantly influence his or her ratings of the physical attractiveness of a possible mate. This helps explains why preferences for body weight should vary according to socio-economic status, as individual preferences depend on situational feelings of resource scarcity. In rural contexts, where resource scarcity is more likely to be prevalent, affective and physiological states associated with individual-level resource availability provide implicit information about collective resource availability, and this information then plays a role in the construction of preferences for a heavier body weight. This hypothesis appears to have firm grounding in the psychological literature: feelings not only often serve as 'information' about the environment, but can also influence behaviour without the engagement of complex cognitive processes.

Evolutionary theory has proved to be a powerful theoretical tool in exploring male and female bodily attractiveness. Slogans like 'biology is destiny' have been used by both supporters and critics of evolutionary theory, which always attracts both philosophic and socio-political criticism. Some aspects of attractiveness may be ingrained in our biology: characteristics associated with evolutionary advantages (for example, a low WHR) seem to be perceived as attractive, although debate still continues. However, while some aspects of bodily attractiveness appear innate, other aspects are clearly influenced by culture and experience. The existence of culturally incongruent behaviours and attitudes, of course, suggests that cultures are not fully-integrated systems or coherent wholes. Rather, cultures can best be conceptualised as 'constantly changing, open systems of attitudes, norms, behaviors, artifacts, and institutions that people reinforce but also continually modify or even challenge through diverse means of participation and engagement' (Kim, and Markus, 1999: 798). There are, however, a few core ideas and themes that connect different parts of a given cultural context and that are shared by the majority of its participants. It is the latter that helps explain the extant findings of cross-cultural psychology with regards to body weight and shape preferences.

ACKNOWLEDGEMENTS

I am grateful to Professor Adrian Furnham for his help with this manuscript.

REFERENCES

Abramson, E. E., and Valene, P. (1991). Media use, dietary restraint, bulimia and attitudes toward obesity: A preliminary study. *British Review of Bulimia and Anorexia Nervosa*, 5, 73-76.

Akan, G., and Greilo, C. (1995). Socio-cultural influences on eating attitudes and behaviours, body image and psychological functioning: A comparison of African-American, Asian-American and Caucasian college women. *International Journal of Eating Disorders*, 18, 181-187.

Andersen, A. E., and DiDomenico, L. (1992). Diet versus shape content of popular male and female magazines: A dose-response relationship to the incidence of eating disorders? *International Journal of Eating Disorders*, 11, 283-287.

Anderson, J. L., Crawford, C. E., Nadeau, J., and Lindgberg, T. (1992). Was the Duchess of Windsor right? A cross-cultural view of the socio-biology of ideals of female body shape. *Ethology and Socio-biology*, 13, 197-227.

Arechiga, J., Prado, C., Canto, M., and Carmenati, H. (2001). Women in transition-menopause and body composition in different populations. *Collective Anthropology*, 25, 443-448.

Baker, D., Sivyer, R., and Towell, T. (1998). Body image dissatisfaction and eating attitudes in visually impaired women. *International Journal of Eating Disorders*, 24, 319-322.

Baker, P. (1997). The soft underbelly of the Abdominis: Why men are obsessed with stomach muscles. In *Pictures of Lily: About Men by Men* (pp. 18-23). Exhibition catalogue, Underwood Gallery, London, September.

Barber, N. (1995). The evolutionary psychology of physical attractiveness: Sexual selection and human morphology. *Ethology and Sociobiology*, 16, 395-424.

Barnett, H. L., Keel, P. K., and Conoscenti, L. M. (2001). Body type preferences in Asian and Caucasian college students. *Sex Roles*, 45, 867-878.

Becker, A. E. (1995). *Body, Self and Society: The View From Fiji*. Philadelphia: University of Pennsylvania Press.

Becker, A. E., and Hamburg, P. (1996). Culture, the media, and eating disorders. *Harvard Review of Psychiatry*, 4, 163-167.

Björntorp, P. (1987). Fat cell distribution and metabolism. In R. J. Wurtman and J. J. Wurtman (Eds.), *Human Obesity* (pp. 66-72). New York: New York Academy of Sciences.

Björntorp, P. (1991). Adipose tissue distribution and function. *International Journal of Obesity*, 15, 67-81.

Björntorp, P. (1997). Body fat distribution, insulin resistance and metabolic disease. *Nutrition*, 13, 795-803.

Botta, R. A. (2003). For your health? The relationship between magazine reading and adolescents' body image and eating disturbances. *Sex Roles*, 48, 389-399.

Brewis, A. A., and McGarvey, S. T. (2000). Body image, body size, and Samoan ecological and individual modernisation. *Ecology of Food and Nutrition*, 39, 105-120.

Brown, P., and Konner, M. J. (1987). An anthropological perspective of obesity. *Annals of the New York Academy of Science*, 499, 29.

Bryant, J., and Zhilman, D. (2002). *Media Effects: Advances in Theory and Research*. Mahwah, NJ: Erlbaum.

Buss, D. (1994). *The Evolution of Desire*. New York: Basic Books.

Buss, D. (1999). *Evolutionary Psychology: The New Science of the Mind*. Boston: Allyn and Bacon.

Buss, D., and Schmitt, P. (1993). Sexual strategies theory: An evolutionary perspective on human mating. *Psychological Review*, 100, 204-232.

Cash, T. F., Cash, D. W., and Butters, J. W. (1983). 'Mirror, mirror on the wall...?': Contrast effects and self-evaluations of physical attractiveness. *Personality and Social Psychology Bulletin*, 9, 351-358.

Collins, J. K., and Plahn, M. R. (1988). Recognition accuracy, stereotypic preference, aversion and subjective judgement of body appearance in adolescents and young adults. *Journal of Youth and Adolescence*, 17, 317-332.

Connaly, J., Sluaghter, V., and Mealy, L. (submitted for publication). Children's preference for waist-to-hip ratio: A developmental strategy.

Crago, M., Shisslak, C. M., and Estes, L. S. (1996). Eating disturbances among American minority groups: A review. *International Journal of Eating Disorders*, 19, 239-248.

Crandall, C. (1994). Prejudice against fat people: Ideology and self-interest. *Journal of Personality and Social Psychology*, 66, 882-894.

Davis, C., and Katzman, M. A. (1999) Perfection as acculturation: Psychological correlates of eating problems in Chinese male and female students living in the United States. *International Journal of Eating Disorders*, 25, 65-70.

Deurenberg, P., Deurenberg-Yap, M., and Guricci, S. (2002). Asians are different from Caucasians and from each other in their body mass index/body fat percentage relationship. *Obesity Reviews*, 3, 141-146.

Ehrenkantz, J., Bliss, E., and Sheard, M. H. (1974). Plasma testosterone: Correlation with aggressive behaviour and social dominance in man. *Psychosomatic Medicine*, 36, 469-475.

Ellisson, P. (1990). Human ovarian function and reproductive ecology: New hypotheses. *American Anthropologist*, 92, 933-952.

Eppright, T. D., Sanfancon, J. A., Beck, N. C., and Bradley, J. S. (1997). Sport psychiatry in childhood and adolescence: An overview. *Child Psychiatry and Human Development*, 28, 71-88.

Faludi, S. (1999). *Stiffed: The Betrayal of the American Man*. New York: W. Morrow, and Co.

Fan, J. T., Dai, W., Liu, F., and Wu, J. (2005). Visual perception of male body attractiveness. *Proceedings of the Royal Society of London B*, 272, 219-226.

Fan, J., Liu, F., Wu, J., and Dai, W. (2004). Visual perception of female physical attractiveness. *Proceedings of the Royal Society of London B*, 271, 347-352.

Field, A. E., Carmago, C. A., Taylor, C. B., Berkey, C. S., Roberts, S. B., and Coldizt, G. A. (2001). Peer, parent and media influences on the development of weight concerns and frequent dieting among preadolescent and adolescent girls and boys. *Paediatrics*, 107, 54-60.

Fitzgibbon, M.L., Spring, B., Avellone, M. E., Blackman, L. R., Pingitore, R., and Stolley, M. R. (1998). Correlates of binge eating in Hispanic, black and white women. *International Journal of Eating Disorders*, 24, 43-52.

Ford, C. S., and Beach, F. A. (1952). *Patterns of Sexual Behaviour*. New York: Harper.

Forestell, C. A., Humphrey, T. M., and Stewart, S. H. (2004). Involvement of body weight and shape factors in ratings of attractiveness by women: A replication and extension of Tassinary and Hansen (1998). *Personality and Individual Differences*, 36, 295-305.

Franzoi, S. L., and Herzog, M. E. (1987). Judging physical attractiveness: What body aspects do we use? *Personality and Social Psychology Bulletin*, 13, 19-33.

Frederick, D. A., and Haselton, M. G. (2003). Muscularity as a communicative signal. Paper presentation at the International Communications Association, San Diego, California.

Freedman, R. E. K., Carter, M. M., Sbrocco, T., and Gray, J. J. (2004). Ethnic differences in preferences for female weight and waist-to-hip ratio: A comparison of African-American and White American college and community samples. *Eating Behaviors*, 5, 191-198.

Frisch, R. E. (1987). Body fat, menarche, fitness and fertility. *Human Reproduction*, 2, 521-533.

Frisch, R. E. (1988). Fatness and fertility. *Scientific American*, 258, 88-95.

Furnham, A., and Alibhai, N. (1983). Cross-cultural differences in the perception of female body-shapes. *Psychological Medicine*, 13, 829-837.

Furnham, A., and Baguma, P. (1994). Cross-cultural differences in the evaluation of male and female body shapes. *International Journal of Eating Disorders*, 15, 81-89.

Furnham, A. F., and Radley, S. (1989). Sex differences in the perceptions of male and female body shapes. *Personality and Individual Differences*, 10, 653-662.

Furnham, A., Dias, M., and McClelland, A. (1998). The role of body weight, waist-to-hip ratio, and breast size in judgments of female attractiveness. *Sex Roles*, 34, 311-326.

Furnham, A., Lavancy, M., and McClelland, A. (2001). Waist-to-hip ratio and facial attractiveness: A pilot study. *Personality and Individual Differences*, 30, 491-502.

Furnham, A., Moutafi, J., and Baguma, P. (2002). A cross-cultural study on the role of weight and waist-to-hip ratio on judgements of women's attractiveness. *Personality and Individual Differences*, 32, 729-745.

Furnham, A., Petrides, K. V., and Constantinides, A. (2005). The effects of body mass index and waist-to-hip ratio on ratings of female attractiveness, fecundity and health. *Personality and Individual Differences*, 38, 1823-1834.

Furnham, A., Tan, T., McManus, C. (1997). Waist-to-hip ratio and preferences for body shape: A replication and extension. *Personal and Individual Differences*, 22, 539-549.

Folsom, A. R., Kaye, S. A., Sellers, T. A., Hong, C., Cerhan, J. R., Potter, J. D., and Prineas, R. (1993). Body fat distribution and 5-year risk of death in older women. *Journal of the American Medical Association*, 269, 483-487.

Garner, D. M., Garfinkel, P. E., Schwartz, D., and Thompson, M. (1980). Cultural expectations of thinness in women. *Psychological Reports*, 47, 483-491.

Ghannam, F. (1997). Fertile, plump and strong: The social construction of female body in low income Cairo. *Monographs in Reproductive Health Number 3.* Cairo: Population Council Regional Office for West Asia and North Africa.

Gordon, R. A. (2000). *Eating Disorders: Anatomy of a Social Epidemic*, 2nd Edition. Cambridge: Blackwell.

Guo, S., Salisbury, S., Roche, A. F., Chumela, W. C., and Siervogel, R. M. (1994). Cardiovascular disease risk factor and body composition: A Review. *Nutrition Research*, 14, 1721-1777.

Harrison, K. (1997). Does interpersonal attraction to thin media personalities promote eating disorders? *Journal of Broadcasting and Electronic Media*, 41, 478-500.

Heinberg, L. J., Thompson, J. K., and Stormer, S. (1995). Development and validation of the Sociocultural Attitudes Towards Appearance Questionnaire. *International Journal of Eating Disorders*, 17, 81-89.

Henss, R. (1995). Waist-to-hip ratio and attractiveness. Replication and extension. *Personality and Individual Differences*, 19, 479-488.

Henss, R. (2000). Waist-to-hip ratio and female attractiveness. Evidence from photographic stimuli and methodological considerations. *Personality and Individual Differences*, 28, 501-513.

Hesse-Biber, S. (1996). *Am I Thin Enough Yet? The Cult of Thinness and the Commercialisation of Identity*. New York: Oxford University Press.

Horvath, T. (1979). Correlates of physical beauty in men and women. *Social Behaviour and Personality*, 7, 145-151.

Huang, Z., Willet, W. C., and Colditz, G. A. (1999). Waist circumference, waist:hip ratio, and risk of breast cancer in the Nurses' Health Study. *American Journal of Epidemiology*, 150, 1316-1324.

Hughes, S. M., and Gallup, G. G. (2003). Sex differences in morphological predictors of sexual behaviour: Shoulder-to-hip and waist-to-hip ratios. *Evolution and Human Behavior*, 24, 173-178.

Hume, D. (1757). *Four Dissertations. IV: Of the Standard of Taste*. London: Millar.

Jones, P. R. M., Hunt, M. J., Brown, T. P., and Norgan, N. G. (1986). Waist-hip circumference ratio and its relation to age and overweight in British men. *Human Nutrition: Clinical Nutrition*, 40C, 239-247.

Kaye, S. A., Folsom, A. R., Prineas, R. J., and Gapstur, S. M. (1990). The association of body fat distribution with lifestyle and reproductive factors in a population study of post-menopausal women. *International Journal of Obesity*, 14, 583-591.

Kim, H., and Markus, H. R. (1999). Deviance or uniqueness, harmony or conformity? A cultural analysis. *Journal of Personality and Social Psychology*, 77, 785-800.

Kirschner, M. A., and Samojlik, E. (1991). Sex hormone metabolism in upper and lower body obesity. *International Journal of Obesity*, 15, 101-108.

Kissebah, A. H., and Krakower, G. R. (1994). Regional adiposity and mortality. *Physiological Review*, 74, 761-811.

Kopelman, P. G. (2000). Obesity as a medical problem. *Nature*, 404, 635-643.

Lake, J. K., Power, C., and Cole, T. J. (1997). Women's reproductive health: The role of body mass index in early and adult life. *International Journal of Obesity*, 21, 432-438.

Lanska, D. J., Lanska, M. J., Hartz, A. J., and Rimm, A. A. (1985). Factors influencing anatomical location of fat tissue in 52,953 women. *International Journal of Obesity*, 9, 29-38.

Lavrakas, P. J. (1975). Female preferences for male physique. *Journal of Research in Personality*, 9, 324-334.

Leder, H. (1996). *Linienzeichnungen von Gesichtern. Verfremdungen im Gesichtsmodul (Line drawings of faces. Distortions in the face module)*. Bern: Huber.

Lee, S., and Lee, A. M. (2000). Disordered eating in three communities of China: A comparative study of female high school students in Hong Kong, Shenzhen, and rural Hunan. *International Journal of Eating Disorders*, 27, 317-327.

Leit, R. A., Pope, H. G. Jr., and Gray, J. J. (2001). Cultural expectations of muscularity in men: The evolution of *Playgirl* centrefolds. *International Journal of Eating Disorders*, 29, 90-93.

Lynch, S. M., and Zellner, D. A. (1999). Figure preferences in two generations of men: The use of figure drawings illustrating differences in muscle mass. *Sex Roles*, 40, 833-843.

Maisey, D. M., Vale, E. L. E., Cornelissen, P. L., and Tovée, M. J. (1999). Characteristics of male attractiveness for women. *Lancet*, 353, 1500.

Malson, H. (1998). *The Thin Woman: Feminism, Post-Structuralism and the Social Psychology of Anorexia Nervosa.* London: Routledge.

Manning, J. T., Anderton, K., and Washington, S. M. (1996). Women's waist and the sex ratio of their progeny: Evolutionary aspects of the ideal female body shape. *Journal of Human Evolution*, 31, 41-47.

Manning, J. T., Trivers, R. L., Singh, D., and Thornhill, A. (1999). The mystery of female beauty. *Nature*, 399, 214-215.

Manson, J. E., Willet, W. C., Stampfer, M. J., Colditz, G. A, Hunter, D. J., Hankinson, S. E., Hennekens, C. H., and Speizer, F. E. (1995). Body weight and mortality among women. *New England Journal of Medicine*, 333, 677-685.

Marlowe, F., and Wetsman, A. (2001). Preferred waist-to-hip ratio and ecology. *Personality and Individual Differences*, 30, 481-489.

Marti, B., Tuomilehto, J., Saloman, V., Kartovaara, H. J., and Pietinen, P. (1991). Body fat distribution in the Finnish population: Environmental determinants and predictive power for cardiovascular risk factor level. *Journal of Epidemiological Community Health*, 45, 131-137.

McCreary, D. R., and Sasse, D. K. (2000). An exploration of the drive for muscularity in adolescent boys and girls. *Journal of American College Health*, 48, 297-320.

McKeigue, P. M., Shah, B., Marmot, M. G. (1991). Relation of central adiposity and insulin resistance with high diabetes prevalence and cardiovascular risk in South Asians. *The Lancet*, 337, 382-386.

Miller, M. N., and Pumariega, A. J. (2001). Culture and eating disorders: A historical and cross-cultural review. *Psychiatry*, 64, 93-110.

Mintz, L. B., and Kashubeck, S. (1999). Body image and disordered eating among Asian-American and Caucasian college students: An examination of race and gender differences. *Psychology of Women Quarterly*, 23, 781-796.

Misra, A., and Vikram, N. (2003). Clinical and pathophysiological consequences of abdominal adiposity and abdominal adipose tissue depots. *Nutrition*, 19, 456-457.

Molarius, A., Seidell, J. C., Sans, S., Tuomilehto, J. R., and Kuulasmaa, K. (1999). Waist and hip circumference, and waist-to-hip ratio in 19 populations of WHO MONICA Project. *International Journal of Obesity*, 23, 116-125.

Morry, M. M., and Staska, S. L. (2001). Magazine exposure: Internalization, self-objectification, eating attitudes, and body satisfaction in male and female university students. *Canadian Journal of Behavioural Sciences*, 33, 269-279.

Murray, S. H., Touyz, S. W., and Beumont, P. J. V. (1996). Awareness and perceived influence of body ideals in the media: A comparison of eating disorder patients and the general community. *Eating Disorders: The Journal of Treatment and Prevention*, 4, 33-46.

Nasser, M. (1986). Comparative study of the prevalence of abnormal eating attitudes among Arab female students of both London and Cairo universities. *Psychological Medicine*, 16, 621-625.

Nasser, M. (1994). Screening for abnormal eating attitudes in a population of Egyptian secondary school girls. *Social Sciences and Medicine*, 42, 21-34.

Nasser, M. (1997). *Culture and Weight Consciousness.* London: Routledge.

Nelson, L. D., and Morrison, E. L. (2005). The symptoms of resource scarcity: Judgements of food and finances influence preference for potential partners. *Psychological Science*, 16, 167-173.

Olivardia, R., Pope, H. G. Jr., Borowiecki, J. J., and Cohane, G. H. (2004). Biceps and body image: The relationship between muscularity and self-esteem, depression, and eating disorder symptoms. *Psychology of Men and Masculinity*, 5, 112-120.

Pasquali, R., Gambineri, A., Anconetani, B., Vicennati, V., Colitta, D., Caramelli, E., Casimirri, F., and Morselli-Labali, A. M. (1999). The natural history of the metabolic syndrome in young women with the polycystic ovary syndrome and the effect on long-term oestrogen-progestagen treatment. *Clinical Endocrinology*, 50, 517-527.

Perez, M., and Joiner, T. E., Jr. (2003). Body image dissatisfaction and disordered eating in Black and White women. *International Journal of Eating Disorders*, 33, 342-350.

Petrie, T. A., Austin, L. J., Crowley, B. J., Helmcamp, A., Johnson, C. E., Lester, R., Rogers, R., Turner, J., and Walbrick, K. (1996). Sociocultural expectations of attractiveness for males. *Sex Roles*, 35, 581-602.

Pirwany, I. R., Fleming, R., Greer, C. J., Packard, C. J., and Sattar, N. (2001). Lipids and lipoprotein subfractions in women with PCOS: Relationship to metabolic and endocrine parameters. *Clinical Endocrinology*, 54, 447-453.

Pond, C. M. (1978). Morphological aspects and the ecological and mechanical consequences of fat deposition in wild vertebrates. *Annual Review of Ecology and Systematics*, 9, 519-570.

Pope, H. G. Jr., Olivardia, R., Gruber, A., and Borowiecki, J. (1999). Evolving ideals of male body image as seen through action toys. *International Journal of Eating Disorders*, 26, 65-72.

Pope, H. G. Jr., Phillips, K. A., Olivardia, R. (2000). *The Adonis Complex: How to Identify, Treat, and Prevent Body Obsession in Men and Boys*. New York: Simon and Schuster.

Poran, M. A. (2002). Denying diversity: Perceptions of beauty and social comparison processes among Latina, Black and White women. *Sex Roles*, 47, 65-81.

Posavac, H. D., Posavac, S. S., and Weigel, R. G. (2001). Reducing the impact of media images on women at risk for body image disturbance: Three targeted interventions. *Journal of Social and Clinical Psychology*, 20, 324-340.

Powers, P. S. (1980). *Obesity: The Regulation of Weight*. Baltimore: Williams and Wilkins.

Puhl, R. M., and Boland, F. J. (2001). Predicting female physical attractiveness: Waist-to-hip ratio versus thinness. *Psychology, Evolution and Gender*, 3, 27-46.

Rebuffé-Scrive, M (1988). Metabolic differences in deposits. In C. Bouchhard and F. E. Johnston (Eds.), *Fat Distribution During Growth and Later Health Outcomes* (pp. 163-173). New York: Alan R. Liss.

Rebuffé-Scrive, M. (1991). Neuroregulation of adipose tissue: Molecular and hormonal mechanisms. *International Journal of Obesity*, 15, 83-86.

Reid, R. L. and van Vugt, D. A. (1987). Weight related changes in reproductive function. *Fertility and Sterility*, 48, 905-913.

Ricciardelli, L. A., and McCabe, M. P. (2001). Self-esteem and negative affect as moderators of sociocultural influences on body dissatisfaction, strategies to decrease weight, and strategies to increase muscles among adolescent boys and girls. *Sex Roles*, 44, 189-206.

Ross, W. D., and Ward, R. (1982). Human proportionality and sexual dimorphism. In R. L. Hall (Ed.), *Sexual Dimorphism in Homo Sapiens: A Question of Size* (pp. 317-361). New York: Praeger.

Rozmus-Wrzesinska, M., and Pawłowski, B. (2005). Men's ratings of female attractiveness are influenced more by changes in female waist size compared with changes in hip size. *Biological Psychology*, 68, 299-308.

Rucker III, C. E., and Cash, T. F. (1992). Body images, body-size perceptions, and eating behaviour among African-Americans and white college women. *International Journal of Eating Disorders*, 12, 291-299.

Rudovsky, B. (1974). *The Unfashionable Human Body*. New York: Anchor Books.

Shackelford, T. K., Weekes-Shackelford, V. A., LeBlanc, G. J., Bleske, A. L., Euler, H. A., and Hoier, S. (2000). Female coital orgasm and male attractiveness. *Human Nature: An Interdisciplinary Biosocial Perspective*, 11, 299-306.

Shetty, P. S., and James, W. P. T. (1994). *Body mass index: A measure of chronic energy deficiency in adults.* Rome: Food and Agriculture Organisation of the United Nations, Food and Nutrition Paper 56.

Silbereisen, R. K., and Kracke, B. (1997). Self-reported maturational timing and adaptation in adolescence. In G. Schulenberg (Ed.), *Health Risks and Developmental Transition During Adolescence* (pp. 85-109). Cambridge, UK: Cambridge University Press.

Singh, D. (1993a). Adaptive significance of female physical attractiveness: Role of waist-to-hip ratio. *Journal of Personality and Social Psychology*, 65, 292-307.

Singh, D. (1993b). Body shape and women's attractiveness. The critical role of waist-to-hip ratio. *Human Nature*, 4, 297-321.

Singh, D. (1994a). Is thin really beautiful and good? Relationship between waist-to-hip ratio (WHR) and female attractiveness. *Personality and Individual Differences*, 16, 123-132.

Singh, D. (1994b). Waist-to-hip ratio and judgements of attractiveness and healthiness of females' figures by male and female physicians. *International Journal of Obesity*, 18, 731-737.

Singh, D. (1994c). Body fat distribution and perception of desirable female body shape by young black men and women. *International Journal of Eating Disorders*, 16, 289-294.

Singh, D. (1994d). WHR and judgements of attractiveness and healthiness by male and female physicians. *International Journal of Obesity*, 18, 731-737.

Singh, D. (1995a). Female judgement of male attractiveness and desirability for relationships: Role of waist-to-hip ratio and financial status. *Journal of Personality and Social Psychology*, 69, 1089-1101.

Singh, D. (1995b). Female health, attractiveness and desirability for relationships: Role of breast asymmetry and WHR. *Ethology and Sociobiology*, 16, 465-481.

Singh, D. (2000). Waist-to-hip ratio: An indicator of female mate value. Paper presented at the Kyoto Symposium on Human Mate Choice. November 20-24.

Singh, D. (2002). Female mate value at a glance: Relationship of waist-to-hip ratio to health, fecundity and attractiveness. *Human Ethology and Evolutionary Psychology*, 23, 81-91.

Singh, D. (2004). Mating strategies of young women: Role of physical attractiveness. *Journal of sex Research*, 41, 43-54.

Singh, D. and Luis, S. (1995). Ethnic and gender consensus for the effect of waist-to-hip ratio on judgements of women's attractiveness. *Human Nature*, 6, 51-65.

Singh, D., and Young, R. K. (1995). Body weight, waist-to-hip ratio, breasts, and hips: Role in judgements of female attractiveness and desirability for relationships. *Ethology and Sociobiology*, 16, 483-507.

Singh, D., and Zambarano, R. J. (1997). Offspring sex ratio in women with android body fat distribution. *Journal of Human Biology*, 69, 545-556.

Singh, D., Davis, M., and Randall, P. (2000, June). Fluctuating ovulation: Lower WHR, enhanced self-perceived attractiveness, and increased sexual desire. Paper presented at Human Evolution and Behaviour Society meeting, London.

Smolak, L., and Levine, M. P. (1996). Developmental transitions at middle school and college. In L. Smolak, M. P. Levine and R. H. Strigel-Moore (Eds.), *The Developmental Psychopathology of Eating Disorders: Implications for Research, Prevention and Treatment* (pp. 207-233). Hillsdale, New Jersey: Erlbaum.

Sobal, J., and Stunkard, A. J. (1989). Socio-economic status and obesity: A review of the literature. *Psychological Bulletin*, 105, 260-275.

Staffieri, J. R. (1967). A study of social stereotypes of body image in children. *Journal of Personality and Social Psychology*, 7, 101-104.

Stam, H. (Ed.) (1998). *The Body and Psychology*. London: Sage.

Streeter, S. A., and McBurney, D. (2003). Waist-hip ratio and attractiveness: New evidence and a critique for a 'critical test.' *Evolution and Human Behaviour*, 24, 88-98.

Sugiyama, L. S. (2004). Is beauty in the context-sensitive adaptations of the beholder? Shiwiar use of waist-to-hip ratio in assessments of female mate value. *Evolution and Human Behaviour*, 25, 51-62.

Swami, V., and Tovée, M. J. (2005a). Female physical attractiveness in Britain and Malaysia: A cross-cultural study. *Body Image*, 2, 115-128.

Swami, V., and Tovée, M. J. (in press). Do judgements of food influence preferences for female body weight? *British Journal of Psychology.*

Swami, V. and Tovée, M. J. (2005b). Male physical attractiveness in Britain and Malaysia: A cross-cultural study. *Body Image, 2,* 383-393.

Swami, V., Caprario, C., Tovée, M. J., and Furnham, A. (in press). A western predicament? Preferences for a slim ideal in Japan and Britain. *European Journal of Personality.*

Swami, V., Furnham, A., Shah, K., Tovée, M. J., and Baguma, P. (submitted). The influence of body weight and shape on female physical attractiveness in Britain and Uganda using biologically valid figures. *Social Sciences and Medicine.*

Swami, V., Knight, D., Tovée, M. J., Davies, P., and Furnham, A. (submitted). Perceptions of female physical attractiveness among Pacific Islanders. *Journal of Cross-Cultural Psychology.*

Swami, V., Tovée, M. J., Furnham, A., and Mangalparsad, R. (submitted). Changing perceptions of attractiveness as observers are exposed to a different culture. *Proceedings of the Royal Society of London B.*

Symons, D. (1995). Beauty is the adaptations of the beholder: The evolutionary psychology of human female sexual attractiveness. In P. R. Abramhamson and S. D. Pinker (Eds.), *Sexual Nature/Sexual Culture* (pp. 80-118). Chicago: Chicago University Press.

Tassinary, L. G., and Hansen, K. A. (1998). A critical test of the waist-to-hip ratio hypothesis of female physical attractiveness. *Psychological Science, 9,* 150-155.

Tovée, M. J., and Cornelissen, P. L. (1999). The mystery of human beauty. *Nature, 399,* 215-216.

Tovée, M. J., and Cornelissen, P. L. (2001). Female and male perceptions of female physical attractiveness in front-view and profile. *British Journal of Psychology, 92,* 391-402.

Tovée, M. J., Brown, J. E., and Jacobs, D. (2001). Maternal waist-hip ratio does not predict child gender. *Proceedings of The Royal Society London B, 268,* 1007-1010.

Tovée, M. J., Emery, J. L., Cohen-Tovée, E. M. (2000). The estimation of body mass index and physical attractiveness is dependent on the observer's own body mass index. *Proceedings of the Royal Society of London B, 267,* 1987-1997.

Tovée, M. J., Hancock, P., Mahmoodi, S., Singleton, B. R. R., and Cornelissen, P. L. (2002). Human female attractiveness: Waveform analysis of body shape. *Proceedings of the Royal Society of London (B), 269,* 2205-2213.

Tovée, M. J., Maisey, D. S., Emery, J. L., and Cornelissen, P. L. (1999). Visual cues to female physical attractiveness. *Proceedings of the Royal Society of London B*, 266, 211-218.

Tovée, M., Mason, S., Emery, J., McCluskey, S., and Cohen-Tovée, E. (1997). Supermodels: Stick insects or hourglasses? *Lancet*, 350, 1474-1475.

Tovée, M. J., Reinhardt, S., Emery, J., and Cornelissen, P. (1998). Optimum body-mass index and maximum sexual attractiveness. *Lancet*, 352, 548.

Wang, J. X., Davies, M., and Norman, R. J. (2000). Body mass and probability of pregnancy during assisted reproduction to treatment: Retrospective study. *Lancet*, 321, 1320-1321.

Wang, Y., Popkin, B., and Thai, F. (1998). The nutritional status and dietary pattern of Chinese adolescents, 1991 and 1993. *European Journal of Clinical Nutrition*, 52, 908-916.

Wass, P., Waldenstrom, U., Rossner, S., and Hellberg, D. (1997). An android body fat distribution in females impairs the pregnancy rate of in-vitro fertilisation-embryo transfer. *Human Reproduction*, 12, 2057-2060.

Wetsman, A. F. (1998). Within- and between-sex variation in human mate choice: An evolutionary perspective. Unpublished doctoral dissertation, University of California, Los Angeles.

Wetsman, A. and Marlowe, F. (1999). How universal are preferences for female waist-to-hip ratios? Evidence from the Hadza of Tanzania. *Evolution and Human Behaviour*, 20, 219-228.

White, P. G., and Gillet, J. (1994). Reading the muscular body – A critical decoding of advertisements in Flex magazine. *Sociology of Sport Journal*, 11, 18-39.

Wilkinson, J., Ben-Tovim, D., and Walker, M. (1994). An insight into the personal significance of weight and shape in large Samoan women. *International Journal of Obesity*, 18, 602-606.

Willet, W. C., Manson, J. E., Stampfer, M. J., Colditz, G. A., Rosner, B., Speizer, F. E., and Hennekens, C. H. (1995). Weight, weight change and coronary heart disease in women: Risk within the 'normal' weight range. *Journal of the American Medical Association*, 273, 461-465.

Wiseman, C. V., Gray, J. J., Mosimann, J. E., and Ahrens, A. H. (1992). Cultural expectations of thinness in women: An update. *International Journal of Eating Disorders*, 11, 85-89.

Van Hooff, M. H., Voorhorst, F. J., Kaptein, M. B., Hirasing, R. A., Koppenaal, C., and Schoemaker, J. (2000). Insulin, androgen and gonadotrophin concentration, body mass index, and waist-to-hip ratio in the first years after menarche in girls with regular menstrual cycle, irregular menstrual cycle, or oligomenorrhea. *Journal of Clinical Endocrinology and Metabolism*, 85, 1394-1400.

Yu, D. W., and Shepard, G. H. (1998). Is beauty in the eye of the beholder? *Nature*, 396, 321-322.

Yu, D. W., and Shepard, G. H. (1999). The mystery of female beauty – Reply. *Nature*, 399, 216.

Zaadstra, B. M., Seidell, J. C., van Noord, P. A. H., te Velde, E. R., Habbema, J. D. F., Vrieswijk, B., and Karbaat, J. (1993). Fat and female fecundity: Prospective study of effect of body fat distribution on conception rates. *British Medical Journal*, 306, 484-487.

In: Exercise and Health Research
Editor: M. D. Johansen, pp. 37-70
ISBN: 978-1-60021-985-6
© 2008 Nova Science Publishers, Inc.

Chapter 2

WHY PHYSICAL EXERCISE SHOULD BE PRESCRIBED IN PANIC DISORDER

Luiz Dratcu

Guy's Hospital, Division of Psychiatry,
Guy's, King's and St Thomas' School of Medical Sciences,
London, United Kingdom

ABSTRACT

A significant progress in understanding the neurochemistry of anxiety has followed the advent of biochemical methods to induce anxiety symptoms. There has been particular interest in panic attacks since the discovery that they may be provoked in the laboratory, and thus are amenable to experimental investigation. For this reason, and because the episodic nature of a panic attack makes the disorder easy to quantify, panic disorder has been extensively studied in the last decades. Another reason why provocation of panic has attracted interest is that, in theory, knowledge gained from such studies can be extrapolated to anxiety in general. While research on the pathogenesis of panic disorder has concentrated on panic attacks, what happens to panic patients in the non-panic state has been largely overlooked. And yet, patients remain clinically unwell between attacks. Panic patients experience background anxiety and they also chronically hyperventilate. Hyperventilation was thought to induce panic by lowering CO_2, but provocation studies using carbon dioxide (CO_2) demonstrated that, in fact, panic patients have hypersensitive CO_2

chemoreceptors. Klein proposed that panic patients hyperventilate in the attempt to keep pCO_2 low, thereby preventing activation of the brain's suffocation alarm and the panic attacks that ensue. However, panic patients in the non-panic state have been shown to have EEG abnormalities, as well as abnormal cerebral blood flow and cerebral glucose metabolism, an indication of cerebral hypoxia. Hyperventilation can indeed induce cerebral hypoxia, as it leads to systemic alkalosis and cerebral vasoconstriction. Cerebral hypoxia contributes to the onset of anxiety symptoms in chronic obstructive pulmonary disease. By chronically hyperventilating, panic patients may likewise risk prolonged exposure to cerebral hypoxia which, in turn, may contribute to symptom chronicity, thereby engendering a self-perpetuating cycle of panic and anxiety symptoms. Panic patients may therefore benefit from adopting more physiological patterns of breathing. Aerobic exercise may help patients to normalise ventilatory patterns and attenuate the adverse effects of chronic hyperventilation on the brain. The role of pharmacological and psychological treatments in anxiety disorders is now well established, but there is evidence that aerobic exercise regularly is itself therapeutic in panic disorder and that it can also effectively augment antipanic treatment. Exercise may prove an adjunct treatment for anxiety disorders that is non-pharmacological, non-addictive, and one that has few adverse effects and contraindications. In addition to reducing the risk of coronary heart disease, stroke and obesity-related disorders, exercise offers a range of psychological benefits.

INTRODUCTION

Physical exercise has been increasingly recommended to patients with psychotic disorders as part of their treatment protocols (Faulkner et al, 2003). This has followed the advent of atypical antipsychotics, whereby concerns about extrapyramidal symptoms associated with the conventional antipsychotics have been superseded by concerns about the increased risk of weight gain and type-2 diabetes which, under the label of metabolic syndrome, has been associated with some of the newer drugs (Stahl, 2002). In addition to curbing drug-induced weight gain and preventing the onset of type-2 diabetes, engaging in physical exercise can prevent cardiovascular disease and osteoporosis (Fentem, 1994) and promote positive changes in the otherwise unhealthy lifestyle that people with severe mental illness tend to adopt (Phelan et al, 2001)

As a group, however, anxiety disorders are by far the most frequent psychiatric disorder (Oakley-Browne, 1991). Like psychotic illness, anxiety disorders also have onset early in life and follow a chronic course, their symptoms can be very impairing, and patients have a range of medical complications and a high rate of service utilization. It is no surprise that the prognosis of anxiety disorders may not always be bright, despite the variety of pharmacological and psychological treatments available. However, perhaps because the clinical presentation of anxiety disorders may not be as dramatic as in schizophrenia, additional measures to improve the quality of life of these patients, including those that may be relevant to their medical status or unresolved chronic symptoms, have not instigated the same attention. And yet, the reasons for prescribing exercise for patients with anxiety disorders are at least as compelling.

Panic disorder is probably the best example to argue this point. If a dimensional approach of pathological anxiety is adopted, the concept of panic disorder seems to encompass those anxious patients at the clinical end of the spectrum, where anxiety states are most distinct and intense. There is good evidence to suggest that panic patients develop abnormal breathing patterns, in particular a propensity to hyperventilate, in association with, and maybe as a result of, their repeated panic attacks. This chapter attempts to substantiate the view that, in the long-term, the combination of panic attacks with dysfunctional respiratory patterns may culminate in a self-perpetuating cycle of panic and anxiety symptoms. If this is true, the therapeutic advantages to panic patients of undergoing breathing retraining are self-evident. Practising aerobic exercise on a regular basis is probably the best and most effective method to restore normal breathing patterns in this patient group. As well as the many benefits it offers generally to both physical and mental health, physical exercise, particularly aerobic exercise, may rectify physiological unbalances that evolve as part of the pathogenesis of panic disorder, and which in turn may be conducive to pernicious changes in cerebral function.

PANIC DISORDER, MORE THAN PANIC ATTACKS ALONE

Panic attacks are paroxysmal episodes of anxiety accompanied by fearful thoughts and activating physical symptoms, such as tachycardia, dyspnoea, tremor, nausea and dizziness (American Psychiatric Association, 1994). Over the past two decades, the prevalence of panic attacks in the general adult US population may have increased to nearly 13% (Goodwin, 2003). Whether or not this might reflect an increase in the prevalence of panic disorder is unclear. Panic disorder, an anxiety disorder where panic attacks are frequent, has a lifetime prevalence of about 2% and high comorbidity with other anxiety disorders, depression and substance abuse disorders (Wittchen and Essau, 1993), significantly eroding everyday quality of life of sufferers (Carpiniello et al, 2002). Severe background anxiety may be the reason why comorbidity of panic disorder with generalised anxiety disorder can be as high as 60-80% (Breier et al, 1986; Cassano et al, 1990). Full remission is possible (Swoboda et al, 2003), especially during the first years of the illness (Yonkers et al, 2003), but panic disorder usually follows a chronic or episodic course (Angst and Vollrath, 1991) and may persist for over 20 years if left untreated (Wittchen and Essau, 1993).

The vast majority of studies on the pathogenesis of panic disorder have concentrated on panic attacks, but changes that occur in the non-panic state are also likely to play a part in the course of the illness. As well as chronic anxiety, panic patients in the non-panic state have a distorted cognitive perception of their bodily and mental functioning and they also tend to hyperventilate (Dratcu and Bond, 1998). Despite the progress that has been made in the clinical management of panic disorder (Pollack et al, 2003), many panic patients still report residual anxiety symptoms following antipanic treatment (Roy-Byrne and Cowley, 1994/1995). Even after apparently achieving a good response to drug treatment, as many as one-third of panic patients experience persistent anxiety and somatic symptoms that may pass undetected in follow-up studies (Corominas et al, 2002). The risk of relapse is also high. In a naturalistic study of 78 panic patients who had achieved remission following drug treatment, half of the patients relapsed at some time over a 2-year period, despite continued pharmacotherapy (Simon et al, 2002). Moreover, even though hyperventilation has long been known to be associated with panic attacks (Gorman et al, 1984; Lum, 1987; Klein, 1993), the clinical implications of chronic hyperventilation, particularly in the long term, remain unclear.

PROVOKING PANIC ATTACKS: A BRIEF HISTORY

Why do some people panic spontaneously? Plausible answers to this question started to surface after the discovery that a number of substances could precipitate panic attacks, and that patients with panic disorder were more susceptible to these agents than healthy subjects or patient with other psychiatric disorders. Experimental research has prompted different models to explain the exacerbated response found in panic patients, nearly as many as the number of mechanisms thought to be involved in the mode of action of panic-provoking agents (see Kahn and Van Praag, 1992; Nutt and Lawson, 1992). Following the pioneer study of Pitts and McClure (1967) using sodium lactate (see below), agents subsequently employed in provocation studies include bicarbonate, noradrenergic compounds, drugs with affinity for benzodiazepine (BDZ)-receptors, caffeine, cholecystokinin, serotonergic agonists and carbon dioxide.

Pharmacological models of panic have been criticised on several grounds. The precise mechanisms of many of the agents used to induce panic are obscure, non-pharmacological factors may be involved in their effects, and it is possible that there are several mechanisms, and not just one, involved in the panicogenic action of a given agent (Gorman et al, 1987). Moreover, the theories derived from the panicogenic effect of a given agent usually fail to explain the effect of all other agents that do not affect the same neurochemical system. The finding that panic patients are susceptible to increases in pCO_2 has opened a new chapter in this field of research.

PANIC AND HYPERSENSITIVE CHEMORECEPTORS: FROM SODIUM LACTATE TO CARBON DIOXIDE

The association of panic disorder with vulnerability to increases in pCO_2 only came to light after twenty years of research using methods to provoke panic experimentally. It is interesting to review briefly how researchers in this field have reached this verdict, as cogent explanations for the pathogenesis of panic disorder have been crafted in the process. It all started with Pitts and McClure's (1967) initiative to test an old hypothesis that anxiety attacks might be produced in susceptible individuals by the rise in blood lactate, for which purpose they infused sodium lactate intravenously into patients suffering from (pre-DSM) anxiety neurosis and normal controls. Lactate precipitated symptoms in patients which 'were markedly similar or identical' to those experienced in their 'worst anxiety attacks'. This finding has been subsequently replicated in a number of studies which showed that infusion of 0.5 to 1 M sodium lactate consistently induced panic attacks in 26-100% of panic patients in contrast to 0-30% of normal controls (Kahn and Van Praag, 1992). The hypothesis that panic patients were simply less fit than healthy subjects has been discounted (Maddock and Mateo-Bermudez, 1990), and so were the original views that the effect of lactate was due to hypocalcaemia (Pitts and McClure, 1967) or that panic patients were hypersensitive to changes in pH (Carr and Sheehan, 1984).

Liebowitz et al (1984, 1985) argued that lactate precipitated panic by inducing metabolic alkalosis and stimulating the respiratory centres, a process in which bicarbonate - which increases peripheral pH and is the penultimate metabolite of lactate - would also be involved. However, although both lactate and bicarbonate provoke panic attacks in panic patients (Gorman et al, 1989), the finding that bicarbonate is less anxiogenic than lactate suggested that panic could not be due to metabolic alkalosis alone. Moreover, metabolic alkalosis due to bicarbonate leads to compensatory hypoventilation, whereas patients hyperventilate during a panic attack. Nonetheless, bicarbonate is further metabolised into CO_2. Carbon dioxide crosses the blood-brain barrier and increases the ventilatory rate by stimulating ventral medullary chemoreceptors. Thus the panicogenic effect of lactate could be partly related to activation of CO_2 chemoreceptors. Indeed, Gorman et al (1988) reported that a 5% CO_2 air mixture inhaled for 20 minutes provoked panic attacks in seven of 12 panic patients but did not in any of four normal controls. This corroborated results of a previous study where a single inhalation of 35% CO_2/65% O_2 given to panic patients and normal subjects instantaneously elicited panic-like symptoms or high levels of anxiety in most of the patients, while control subjects rarely rated their symptoms as anxiety (Griez et al, 1987). Griez et al (1990) further investigated this by administering 35% CO_2 or compressed air (as a placebo) to panic patients, patients with obsessive-compulsive and normal controls. Increases in panic symptoms were significant in all groups, but while the obsessive-compulsive patients and the control subjects did not differ from each other, ratings for panic symptoms were significantly higher for panic patients as compared to both.

Gorman et al (1988) conjectured that panic patients have abnormally sensitive medullary chemoreceptors. These chemoreceptors, which normally induce increased ventilation when pCO_2 rises (hypercapnia), could be activated at lower levels of CO_2 in panic patients. However, rather than revealing differences in physiological sensitivity to CO_2 per se, panic attacks in response to either a decrease or increase of pCO_2 could still be seen as resulting from 'catastrophic' cognitive misinterpretations that patients make of the peripheral changes induced by manipulation of CO_2 either way (Bass, 1987; Gelder, 1987). A comprehensive review of the catastrophic misinterpretation model of panic can be found elsewhere (Austin and Richards, 2001).

Papp et al (1993b) attempted to ascertain whether it is CO_2 specifically, and not the distress of breathlessness, which precipitates attacks in panic patients. Responses of panic patients, patients with social phobia and normal controls to inhalation of a mixture of 35% CO_2/65% O_2 for 30 seconds were compared to their responses to a procedure in which subjects had to breathe for 30 seconds through a valve reducing the diameter of the airway. Carbon dioxide inhalation proved significantly more potent than increased airway resistance in provoking panic in the patient group, but panic patients were significantly more sensitive to

CO_2 than were the patients with social phobia or normal subjects. The CO_2 challenge has subsequently proved to meet the criteria for a good panicogenic (Gorman et al, 1987). Carbon dioxide-induced attacks: are a safe research procedure (Harrington et al, 1996); can be blocked by treatment using selective serotonin reuptake inhibitors (SSRIs), which also block naturally occurring panic (Pols et al, 1996); have good test-retest reliability (Verburg et al, 1998); are not influenced by the experimental setting (Welkowitz et al, 1999); and have been successfully replicated in different groups of panic patients (Biber et al, 1999).

PANIC, HYPERVENTILATION AND THE BRAIN'S ASPHYXIATION ALARM

Hyperventilation is observed in panic patients both during and between panic attacks (Gorman et al, 1984) and has itself has been thought to provoke panic by lowering of pCO_2 and inducing respiratory alkalosis (Lum, 1987). However, this was directly disproved by Garssen et al (1996), who used a fear-provoking situation to induce hyperventilation in a group of 28 panic patients. From a total of 24 panic attacks observed in the study, only one was associated with a fall in pCO_2. So why do panic patients hyperventilate?

Papp et al (1993a) postulated that panic disorder might be due to an unstable autonomic nervous system coupled with cognitive distress. Accordingly, hyperventilation and CO_2 hypersensitivity may be manifestations of a hypersensitive brain stem autonomic control mechanism, whereby challenges that trigger this control mechanism result in acute hyperventilation. Secondary hyperventilatory symptoms, such as chest pain and derealisation, may frighten some vulnerable patients into catastrophic thinking, thus intensifying the panic experience. An alternative explanation for the association between CO_2 hypersensitivity and hyperventilation in panic disorder was formulated by Klein (1993, 1996), who suggested that CO_2 chemoreceptors are linked to a specific alarm and escape mechanism sensitive to asphyxiation that is erroneously triggered in panic patients. Thus spontaneous panic may be a specific false alarm due to a misfiring suffocation alarm: a sudden, misplaced and distressing response to slight increases in pCO_2. In line with this theory, chronic hyperventilation is protective against panic by keeping pCO_2 below the suffocation release threshold. Klein (1993) also differentiated panic induced by yohimbine, caffeine, m-CPP, flumazenil and inverse BDZ agonists from panic induced by lactate, bicarbonate and carbon dioxide. He claimed that, as in acute fear and uncontrollable stress, the former is associated with hypothalamus-pituitary-adrenal (HPA) axis activation and increased cortisolaemia, but not with respiratory symptoms. Only the latter, which is associated with dyspnoea and lack of HPA activation, Klein stated, is truly similar to naturally occurring panic, where the spontaneous 'suffocation alarm' concept is valid. Consistent with this view, Biber and Alkin (1999) reported an experiment in which panic patients with prominent respiratory symptoms were found to be significantly more sensitive to the CO_2 challenge than panic patients with the nonrespiratory subtype of attacks. However, Klein's model has been contested by results of some other studies.

First, in an experiment comparing the thresholds and sensitivities of the central and peripheral chemoreflexes during three re-breathing tests, namely training, hyperoxic (central chemoreflex alone) and hypoxic (combined and central chemoreflex), Katzman et al (2002) found no differences between panic patients and healthy volunteers. Klein's hypothesis would have predicted otherwise. Second, the 35% carbon dioxide challenge does not necessarily discriminate panic disorder from other anxiety disorders. Verburg et al (1995) assessed the responses of nine panic patients with those of nine patients with generalised anxiety disorder to inhalation of a 35% CO_2/65% O_2 mixture. Panic patients experienced a significantly stronger increase in subjective anxiety than generalised anxiety patients but increases in panic symptoms were high in both groups. Similarly, Cardirola et al (1997) compared the effects of the 35% CO_2 inhalation in a group of panic patients and a group of patients with social phobia. Both groups had a similar anxiogenic response to the challenge.

On balance, however, after years of extensive research on the topic, the evidence available does favour the view that sensitivity to CO_2 is a key component of the pathogenesis of panic disorder, but perhaps of other anxiety disorders as well (for critical review, see Rassovsky and Kushner, 2003). Although hyperventilation may offer some protection against panic attacks, does it affect the course of panic disorder?

THE RESPIRATORY PSYCHOPHYSIOLOGY OF PANIC DISORDER

If Klein's theory of a dysfunctional suffocation alarm for panic disorder is correct, hyperventilation represents a physiological adjustment that patients adopt in the attempt to keep pCO_2 low. This protects patients from a hypersensitive suffocation alarm that can misfire in response to fluctuations in pCO_2. It follows that panic patients would tend to become chronic hyperventilators. But do they?

Gorman et al (2001) demonstrated that once a panic attack is triggered by CO_2 inhalation, both minute ventilation and respiratory rates increase regardless of whether or not the subject has panic disorder. Yet it is unclear whether this abnormal ventilatory pattern persists in panic patients between panic attacks. Sinha et al (2000) pointed to evidence suggesting that respiratory physiology is normal in panic patients and that their tendency to hyperventilate and to react with panic to CO_2 represents the triggering of a hypersensitive fear network. In this case, however, hyperventilation in panic patients should be episodic, short-lived and only about as frequent as their panic attacks. Still, according to a growing and persuasive body of research, it seems increasingly clear that, if panic patients do not constantly hyperventilate, they do sustain breathing abnormalities in the long-term, and that respiratory psychophysiology plays a prominent role in panic disorder (Ley, 2001).

For example, a series of studies conducted by Wilhelm et al (2001a,b,c) have shown that respiration is particularly unstable in panic patients. In a comparison of physiological indices in patients with panic disorder, generalised anxiety disorder and healthy subjects, both patient groups reported more anxiety and cardiac symptoms than control subjects, but some somatic symptoms, including breathlessness, were elevated only in panic patients (Wilhelm et al, 2001b). Relative to the control group, mean end-tidal pCO_2 and respiratory rates were lower in panic patients, while their number of sighs was significantly higher. Moreover, tidal volume instability was greater in panic patients than in the two other groups. Wilhelm at al (2001c) subsequently concluded that hypocapnia in panic patients is related to sigh frequency. Not only were panic patients found to sigh more frequently than control subjects, but their sigh breaths were also larger. After sighs, pCO_2 and tidal volume did not return to baseline levels as quickly in panic patients as in control subjects. Finally, Wilhelm at al (2001a) reported that panic and social phobia patients experience more distress than control subjects to hypocapnia induced by fast breathing, but panic patients differ from the two groups in having slower symptomatic and physiological recovery.

Other approaches have also been pursued to investigate respiratory abnormalities in panic disorder. Persistently irregular breathing patterns in panic patients were described that appear to be intrinsic and stable, uninfluenced by doxapram-induced hyperventilation or cognitive manipulation (Abelson et al, 2001). Consistent with this, Martinez et al (2001) found that panic patients have significantly greater respiratory variability at baseline than control subjects or patients with minor depression. Moreover, panic patients with greater respiratory variability were more susceptible to the 7% CO_2 inhalation challenge. Caldirola et al (2004) further confirmed that panic patients have greater entropy in baseline respiratory patterns, indicating higher levels of irregularity and complexity in their respiratory function, while Yeragani et al (2004) demonstrated that existing irregular breathing patterns in panic patients might be changed by antipanic medication (paroxetine). Finally, breathing abnormalities in panic disorder have themselves been the target of specific therapeutic interventions which, under the name of respiratory biofeedback-assisted therapy (Meuret et al, 2001) or breathing training (Meuret et al, 2004), have achieved variable degrees of success (Meuret et al, 2003).

Can the aberrant breathing seen in panic patients be reconciled with Klein's model of panic disorder, which predicts that these patients should frequently hyperventilate? Probably yes. On the one hand, it seems beyond dispute that, whether or not the subject has panic disorder, panic attacks that are provoked by the activation of CO_2 chemoreceptors are followed by increased respiratory rates, a physiological response that reduces pCO_2 (Gorman et al, 2001). On the other hand, because CO_2 chemoreceptors are hypersensitive in panic disorder, panic patients are particularly susceptible to CO_2-induced panic, and hence prone to hyperventilate, at least as frequently as they experience panic attacks. Repeated panic attacks, the core feature of panic disorder, may therefore become increasingly associated with hyperventilation, as it offers patients a physiological protection against, or a mechanism to curtail, panic attacks. However, it is highly unlikely that over the years this association will remain confined to isolated events exclusively. On the contrary, as panic disorder is chronic, and bearing in mind that hyperventilation is a spontaneous activity over which patients may not exert much control, at some stage hyperventilation is bound to also occur separately from panic attacks, the repetition of which can only reinforce this trend. As the illness follows its course, patients will gradually incorporate hyperventilation as part of their habitual breathing, the pattern of which is likely to change. A series of secondary respiratory adjustments, which may be functional or not, is likely to unfold. Over time, this may culminate in an irregular and complex pattern of breathing that may not always reflect the original association of hyperventilation with panic attacks that has triggered the process, but of which frequent sighing, and the ensuing hypocapnia, is a close and constant reminder (Wilhelm et al, 2001b,c).

THE PANIC SYNDROME, HYPERVENTILATION AND THE BRAIN

Do abnormal breathing patterns have any clinical significance in panic disorder? Is a distorted respiratory function only a minor concomitant of the illness, with no impact on its symptoms and progress, and therefore one that can be safely ignored? There are no definite answers at present, mainly because so far experimental research on panic disorder has been largely concerned with panic attacks. From a clinical perspective, however, two major clues do suggest that, most probably, having an abnormal breathing pattern *is* implicated in the course and complications of panic disorder. First, panic patients are unlikely to develop irregular breathing, particularly a propensity to hyperventilate, independently from their panic attacks, but rather as an integral part of the panic syndrome (Klein, 1993; Wilhelm et at, 2001 a,b,c). In addition to panic attacks, panic disorder is associated with anticipatory anxiety, phobic avoidance, medically unexplained medical symptoms, comorbidity with agoraphobia and major depression, and possibly an increased risk of both cardiovascular disease and suicide (Pollack et al, 2003). Second, panic disorder is chronic (Angst and Vollrath, 1991), and panic patients are therefore likely to experience dysfunctional breathing for at least as long as their illness may last. At the same time, there is sufficient evidence to indicate that *cerebral activity is impaired* in panic patients when they are assessed in the *non-panic state*. If anything, dysfunctional breathing, an intrinsic and long-lasting feature of the panic syndrome, may contain a plausible explanation as to why this happens.

It is well established that hyperventilation induces systemic alkalosis, cerebral vasoconstriction, reduced cerebral blood flow and cerebral hypoxia (Lishman, 1998). For this reason, hyperventilation increases slow-wave activity on the electroencephalogram (EEG). In a comparison of physiological indices in unmedicated panic patients in the non-panic state and healthy subjects, patients were found to have significantly more slow-wave activity on the EEG. (Dratcu and Bond, 1998). Patients also rated themselves as feeling significantly more breathless than their normal counterparts. Unfortunately, no measure was taken to confirm whether patients' self-ratings of breathlessness meant that they were actually hyperventilating. However, a previous study of nine anxious patients diagnosed as suffering from hyperventilation syndrome and who were presenting with unilateral somatic symptoms, only two of whom had a formal diagnosis of panic disorder, had shown similar results (O'Sullivan et al, 1992). At this time, the diagnosis of hyperventilation syndrome was validated by an end-tidal pCO_2 of less than 30 mmHg at rest. Six of the nine patients were found to have an abnormal excess of EEG slow-wave activity. Voluntary overbreathing not only exacerbated the slow waves in those patients who already had an excessive EEG slow-wave activity in the resting state, but also produced slow-wave activity in two of the three patients whose EEG was normal at baseline. Panic patients are thus potentially exposed to long periods of EEG slow-wave activity if they hyperventilate chronically. In other words, by chronically hyperventilating, panic patients may risk prolonged exposure to cerebral hypoxia.

Admittedly, results of a couple of small EEG studies can hardly be regarded as strong evidence that dysfunctional breathing alters cerebral function in panic patients. However, this claim finds further support in brain imaging studies of panic patients in the non-panic state, which have consistently demonstrated abnormalities involving both cerebral blood flow (CBF) and cerebral glucose metabolism.

THE PANIC SYNDROME: CEREBRAL DYSFUNCTION IN THE NON-PANIC STATE

In the pioneer of panic disorder using photon emission tomography (PET), Reiman et al (1984) reported that panic patients who had had a panic response to lactate infusion showed an abnormal asymmetry of CBF (left less than right) in the parahippocampal gyrus. Similar results were obtained when, compared with panic patients who did not panic following lactate infusion or normal controls, patients who were vulnerable to lactate were found to have abnormal hemispheric asymmetry of parahippocampal flow, blood volume and oxygen metabolism (Reiman et al, 1986). Also using PET scanning to compare cerebral glucose metabolism in panic patients in the non-panic state and healthy subjects, Nordahl et al (1990) detected asymmetry in the hippocampal region in patients, but no evidence of global metabolic differences in grey matter. However, patients showed metabolic decreases in the left parietal lobule and anterior cyngulate, and increased metabolic rates in the medial orbital frontal cortex. Another similar study observed that panic patients had abnormal brain metabolism of glucose in the hippocampal and parahippocampal areas (Bisaga et al, 1998). Finally, in an attempt to assess the effect of antipanic treatment on the brain's glucose metabolism of panic patients, Nordahl et al (1998) compared regional cerebral glucose metabolic rates (rCMRglc) in a group of unmedicated patients with a group receiving imipramine. Both groups were similarly found to have abnormally low left-right hippocampal rCMRglc ratios, a feature that seemed unaffected by imipramine treatment.

Recent studies employing brain imaging techniques other than PET scanning have also shown anomalous CBF in panic patients. Near-infrared reflection spectroscopy of left and right frontal regions of the brain revealed that the left frontal oxyhemoglobin in panic patients was significantly lower than in control subjects, regardless as to whether or not the stimuli both groups were confronted with were anxiety-eliciting (Akiyoshi et al, 2003). Eren et al (2003), in turn, used Tc99m-hexamethylprpyleneamine oxime single photon emission tomography (SPECT) imaging to compare regional CBF changes in panic patients and control subjects. Patients were reported to have decreased perfusion in the bilateral frontal regions, but a relative increase in perfusion in the right medial and superior frontal regions.

The alterations in CBF and glucose metabolism that panic patients were found to have in these studies cannot be ascribed to panic attacks, as patients were all examined in the non-panic state. Rather, these results seem to be pointing to persistent abnormalities associated with the non-panic state that appear not to change even in response to antipanic treatment, to the extent of being regarded by Nordahl et al (1998) as possibly a 'trait' of panic disorder. Brain PET studies performed *during* panic attacks seem to produce a different picture. For example, Reiman et al (1989) observed that CBF increased bilaterally in several areas of the brain during lactate-induced attacks in panic patients. This may be related to the finding that lactate-induced panic may facilitate the release of atrial natriuretic hormone, a vasodilator and inhibitor of sympathetic activity (Seier et al, 1997).

A SELF-PERPETUATING CYCLE IN PANIC DISORDER: RESPIRATORY AND CEREBRAL DYSFUNCTION

So, could the abnormal CBF and cerebral glucose metabolism in panic patients be associated with effects on the brain of chronic hyperventilation? To be sure, no direct evidence to this effect is available in brain PET studies. There is however evidence that hyperventilation can reduce CBF. Mountz et al (1989) reported that patients with a diagnosis of simple phobia had a significant decrease in global and regional CBF during state anxiety induced by exposure to a fear-provoking stimulus. The decrease in CBF was identified as being an effect of hyperventilation and the ensuing hypocapnia. In another study, Cameron et al (1990) examined the effect of a 250 mg mean dose of caffeine (an anxiogenic agent) on CBF of healthy subjects. Although the dose of caffeine was followed by a 30% decrease of CBF in the whole brain, as compared with baseline measures, caffeine had induced a significant reduction in paCO$_2$ in subjects *before* they were scanned. As subjects presumably hyperventilated after receiving caffeine, the decrease of CBF was most probably an effect of hypocapnia rather than a direct effect of the dose of caffeine. In panic disorder proper, this issue was only marginally addressed in a more recent experiment where [150]water imaging was used to determine global CBF (gCBF) in panic patients and healthy control subjects after inhalations of medical grade air and 35%/65% CO_2/O_2 mixture (Ponto et al, 2002). Still, although no difference was found in pCO$_2$ value between control subjects and patients, panic patients exhibited a decrease in gCBF and stable pCO$_2$-adjusted values in comparisons of air and CO$_2$ inhalations, whereas the control group exhibited stable gCBF and increasing pCO2-adjusted gCBF values.

Findings of these imaging studies are not entirely uniform, but this obviously does not preclude abnormal breathing patterns as the main factor for the cerebral dysfunction that they have detected in panic patients. On the contrary, such imaging studies could hardly be expected to delineate a homogeneous picture of localised dysfunctional areas in the brain. This is because, as panic disorder is chronic, the abnormalities in CBF and cerebral glucose metabolism found in panic patients in the non-panic state may represent the *end result* of the more immediate effects on the brain of hyperventilation *combined* with long-term effects that might develop following prolonged periods of cerebral hypoxia. It could be argued that some of these irregularities in brain activity might have already been present in these patients *before* the onset of their illness, a 'trait' that could be of both primary aetiological significance and predictive value to panic disorder, but three strong arguments suggest otherwise. First, not a single piece of evidence is available that can prove this, at least to our knowledge. Moreover, prospective studies required for this purpose would be impractical and, at any rate, highly unlikely to materialise in the near future. Second, some of the studies above describe a *dynamic and simultaneous* relationship between hyperventilation and changes in brain functioning (Mounty et al, 1989; Cameron et al, 1990; O'Sullivan, 1992). The other studies which do not cannot exclude hyperventilation or other respiratory factors as a plausible explanation for their findings, simply because they did not assess patients' breathing. Third, the fact that panic disorder can be successfully treated, and full symptom remission can be achieved (Swoboda et al, 2003), is not easily reconciled with the notion these patients may suffer from 'inherited', innate life-long anomalies in brain oxygenation or metabolism.

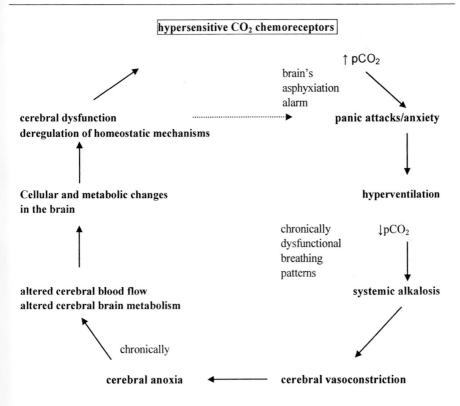

Figure 1. Panic attacks, hypersensitive CO_2 chemoreceptors and hyperventilation. A physiological model for a self-perpetuating cycle within the pathogenesis of panic disorder

Conversely, if abnormal CBF and abnormal cerebral brain metabolism actually *evolve* in panic patients as a *consequence* of a dysfunctional respiratory pattern, as contended in this chapter, these *changes* could have clinical implications in the long-term that may account for important aspects of the panic syndrome (Dratcu, 2000). In theory, cerebral dysfunction secondary to chronically irregular breathing can be construed as part of a cycle that may aggravate, complicate or prolong the symptomatology of panic disorder (*Figure 1*). Compelling indications that this indeed may happen can be found in other medical conditions where anxiety symptoms arise in association with respiratory dysfunction, namely the respiratory diseases themselves.

Panic Disorder, Chronic Pulmonary Obstructive Disease and Cerebral Hypoxia: A Common Path to Chronic Anxiety?

Panic disorder and respiratory diseases seem to be closely related (Goodwin and Pine, 2002). Moreover, this relationship runs both ways. On the one hand, studies on panic disorder have shown that abnormal patterns of respiratory activity are implicated in panic attacks themselves, be they naturally occurring or provoked experimentally. On the other hand, sufferers of respiratory diseases, particularly chronic pulmonary obstructive disease (COPD), experience panic and other anxiety disorders far more frequently than the general population. Having both self-reported respiratory disease and another lung disease increases 4-fold the risk of panic attacks (Goodwin and Pine, 2002).

Respiratory physiology may be involved in the pathogenesis of panic by mechanisms such as the anxiogenic effects of hyperventilation, catastrophic misinterpretations of respiratory symptoms, and neurobiological sensitivity to lactate, CO_2 or other signs of suffocation (Smoller et al, 1996). For instance, panic patients with a lower level of pulmonary function are the subgroup most likely to experience respiratory and fear symptoms during panic attacks (Asmundson and Stein, 1994). Moreover, panic patients who hyperventilate are more susceptible to lactate-induced attacks. In the study of Reiman et al (1986), panic patients who were vulnerable to lactate, and who were found to have abnormal hemispheric asymmetry in the non-panic state, were also described as being abnormally susceptible to episodic hyperventilation. Coplan et al (1998) compared baseline pre-lactate infusion measures of a large group of panic patients who panicked following the lactate challenge with those of panic patients who did not panic and healthy subjects. Patients who panicked in response to lactate were found to have higher levels of hyperventilation and self-reported fear and dyspnoea at baseline, as well as lower levels of pCO_2. Suggestively, baseline scores of fear correlated inversely with pCO_2 levels, and hence positively with hyperventilation. These results are consistent with previous research showing that the three most predictive symptoms of lactate-induced panic are feelings of fear, dyspnoea and desire to flee (Goetz et al, 1996). Similar findings are obtained when the CO_2 challenge is used instead of lactate (Biber and Alkin, 1999).

In turn, patients presenting with respiratory complaints *usually* report anxiety and panic symptoms as well, to the extent that pulmonary disease could be seen as a risk factor for panic disorder, especially when it involves repeated episodes of dyspnoea and life threatening exacerbation of pulmonary dysfunction, coupled with repeated episodes of hypercapnia or hyperventilation (Smoller et al, 1996). In line with this, there is a significant association between asthma, severe asthma and panic attacks, among both adults (Goodwin and Eaton, 2003) and younger people in the general population (Goodwin et al, 2003). Perhaps not surprisingly, panic disorder is common in patients with chest pain who seek help from hospital emergency departments (Wulsin et al, 2002; Huffman and Pollack, 2003). However, of all respiratory diseases, COPD is probably the single diagnostic category that shares more in common with the full spectrum of the panic syndrome (Goodwin and Pine, 2002).

Not only are rates of both panic disorder and generalised anxiety disorder higher in patients with COPD than in the general population, but pharmacological and psychological interventions that are used to treat anxiety disorders are also helpful in COPD (Brenes, 2003). The rate of psychiatric morbidity in COPD patients can be as high as 58%, more than half of which, or one third of all COPD patients, accounted for by panic or other anxiety disorders (Yellowlees et al, 1987; Porzelius et al, 1992). An estimated 8% lifetime prevalence of panic disorder (meeting DSM criteria) in COPD patients is about four times as high as in the general population (Karajgi et al, 1990). Moreover, antipanic agents like alprazolam (Greene et al, 1989; Shivaram et al 1989), tricyclic antidepressants (Borson et al, 1992) and SSRIs (Smoller et al, 1998) have all been shown to ameliorate both *anxiety and respiratory symptoms* in these patients.

A further and particularly significant commonality between panic and COPD patients may lie in the origin of the persistent anxiety observed in both patient groups. Respiratory dysfunction in COPD reduces the supply of oxygen to the brain (Lishman, 1998) and COPD sufferers usually become chronically anxious by the time that hypoxia has become chronic (Borak et al, 1991; Kellner et al, 1992). If prolonged exposure to cerebral hypoxia is implicated in the causation of anxiety in COPD patients, the same principle may in theory also apply to panic patients. If it is true that, as a result of chronic hyperventilation, panic patients may develop cerebral hypoxia, this may likewise account for much of the chronic anxiety that accompanies panic disorder. Indeed, some further similarities between COPD and panic disorder suggest that, in both cases, chronic anxiety probably emerges from an analogous cycle of dysfunctional breathing and cerebral hypoxia. First, levels of anxiety COPD patients seem to be closely associated with the severity of their dyspnoea (Gift and Cahill, 1990), thereby mirroring the association of panic symptoms and respiratory dysfunction that is seen in panic disorder. Second, both dyspnoea and anxiety in COPD patients *subside concomitantly* when patients engage in treatment programmes involving physical exercise (Carrieri-Kohlman et al, 1996). Again, the same is true in panic disorder. As discussed below, panic and anxiety symptoms abate in panic patients when they adhere to routines of physical exercise. The neurorespiratory mechanisms that contribute to the anxiolytic effects of physical exercise in both COPD and panic disorder are a matter for debate. However, a convincing indication that neurophysiological changes play a part in the psychological effects of exercise therapy comes from the benefits it has shown to offer when prescribed in many psychiatric disorders other than panic disorder alone.

EXERCISE THERAPY IN PSYCHIATRIC DISORDERS

Physical exercise has long been recognised as therapeutic in depressive disorder (Hales and Davis, 1987; Martinsen et al, 1989), probably the psychiatric disorder where its effectiveness has been most extensively investigated (Martinsen, 1990; North et al, 1990; Veale et al, 1992). Reviews on the use of exercise therapy in depression have consistently concluded that, provided it is done regularly, both aerobic and non-aerobic forms of exercise significantly reduce depressive symptoms; the more the patients exercise, the greater this effect, which also becomes more prominent the more severe the depression is (North et al, 1990; Martinsen, 1993 and 1994). Moreover, depressed patients usually appreciate exercise therapy, and most continue to exercise after their training programmes are terminated. Those who continue to exercise maintain lower ratings of depression than those who do not.

Crucially, older age is not an impediment to exercise therapy in depression. This has been demonstrated in a recent well designed, randomised controlled study on the effects of exercise in a group of older adults, all of whom suffered from major depression that was poorly responsive to antidepressant medication (Mather et al, 2002). In addition to antidepressants, half of the group was commenced on a 10-week exercise programme, while the other half received talks on health education. After 10 weeks, 55% of the patients who had exercised had successfully achieved a therapeutic response as compared with only one third of the patients in the control subgroup, a difference that not only reached statistical significance but was also maintained for several months after completion of the programme. In short, contemporary empirical evidence on the effects of physical exercise in depression confirms that the ancient adage *mens sana in corporis sano* still holds true.

It also holds true in those clinical conditions whose affective gist lies within the vicinity of the depressive disorders, like the chronic fatigue syndrome. Fulcher and White (1997) demonstrated that a 12-week graded aerobic exercise programme was therapeutic in the chronic fatigue syndrome and that patients showed sustained benefit one year after exercise treatment. Revealingly, another study comparing the effects of exercise and fluoxetine in the chronic fatigue syndrome concluded that, while fluoxetine treatment improved only depressive symptoms, exercise therapy improved both functional activity and fatigue (Wearden et al, 1998). Educating patients about symptoms of the chronic fatigue syndrome offers additional gains, as it encourages self-managed graded exercise (Powell et al, 2001). Moreover, physical exercise such as aerobics floor classes, tennis and brisk walking can similarly alleviate somatic and psychological symptoms commonly associated with premenstrual dysphoric disorder. In a study of the advantages of exercise in menopausal and perimenopausal middle-aged women, exercising women were found to have a significantly more positive mood than sedentary women, regardless of menopausal state (Slaven and Lee, 1997). Exercising women also had less somatic symptoms and less memory or concentration difficulties than women who were physically inactive.

The list of psychiatric disorders that are responsive to physical exercise extends beyond the spectrum of those chraracterised by prominent affective symptoms. Physical exercise can also attenuate the psychopathology associated with psychotic disorders or addictive behaviours. In schizophrenia, for example, programmes of aerobic exercise like cycling performed regularly at least twice a week seem to promote several constructive changes (Pelham and Campagna, 1991), ranging from patients' increased self-esteem to reducing the psychological impact of auditory hallucinations (Faulkner and Sparkes, 1999). Jogging and other forms of aerobic exercise have also proved to be a useful therapeutic resource to people with alcohol and substance misuse disorders (Gary and Guthrie, 1972; Preedy and Peters, 1990). *Table 1* summarises the psychological effects of exercise therapy in psychiatric disorders generally. What are the effects of physical exercise in panic disorder?

Table 1. Psychological and other related benefits of physical exercise regularly

↓ depression	↑ self-esteem
↓ anxiety	↑ motivation
↓ panic attacks	↑ social reintegration
↓ somatic symptoms	↑ physical health
↓ aggressive behaviour	↑ aerobic fitness
↓ perception of mental symptoms	↑ sleep pattern

Exercise Therapy, a Tailor-Made Treatment for Panic Disorder?

The literature on the treatment of panic disorder, as subsumed in recent reviews on the subject, exalts the advantages of drug treatment (Mathew et al, 2001; Sheehan, 2002), cognitive-behavioural therapy, or CBT (Nadiga et al, 2003), and particularly the combination of both (Culpepper, 2004; Doyle and Pollack, 2004; Pollack et al, 2003). Sadly, a Medline search of about 800 publications on panic disorder from 2000 to 2004 will uncover just a few meagre results on the use of exercise therapy in panic patients. Few as they are, these results are nevertheless encouraging.

Broocks et al (1998) randomly assigned 46 panic patients to a 10-week treatment programme of regular aerobic exercise (running), clomipramine 112.5 mg/day (an effective antipanic agent), or placebo tablets. One-third of the patients dropped out from the exercise and placebo groups, but none from the clomipramine group. Regular aerobic exercise alone was associated with significant clinical improvement in panic patients, although it was less effective than treatment using clomipramine. Both exercise and clomipramine treatments significantly reduced patients' symptoms, including depressive symptoms, but clomipramine ameliorated anxiety symptoms significantly earlier and more effectively than exercise (see also Bandelow et al, 2000). The same group of researchers later employed a similar treatment protocol to study the neuroendocrine mechanisms involved in the therapeutic response of panic patients to clomipramine and aerobic exercise (Broocks et al, 2003). For this purpose, the blunted neuroendocrine and psychophysiological responses of panic patients to oral ipsapirone 0.3 mg/kg (a $5\text{-}HT1_A$ receptor agonist) were assessed before and after treatment programmes using clomipramine, aerobic exercise and placebo. After the 10-week treatment period, the psychological responses to ipsapirone were significantly reduced in the clomipramine and the exercise groups, but the hypothermic response to ipsapirone was significantly reduced in the clomipramine group only. These results were tentatively interpreted as an indication that different biological mechanisms are involved in the therapeutic effects of aerobic exercise and clomipramine in panic disorder, respectively.

Table 2. Possible modes of action of exercise therapy

• **hyperthermic model** ↑ body temperature → hypothalamic responses: ↓ muscle tension + ↑ slow wave sleep
• **endorphin hypothesis** ↑ release of β-endorphins → positive affective states
• **self-esteem and mastery explanations** ↑ physical ability → ↑ self-estimation →↑ self-esteem ↑ proprioceptive feedback of body functional abilities
• **distraction hypothesis**
• **central nervous system monoamine activity (↑)**

Aerobic exercise has also proved an effective adjunctive treatment in a group of female patients, aged from 38 to 47 years old, who met DSM-IV criteria (American Psychiatric Association, 1994) for panic disorder, with a duration of illness spanning for over 25 years (Dratcu, 2001). In two of the patients the illness had followed a particularly crippling course, associated with protracted periods of severe agoraphobia and major depression. After receiving various pharmacological and psychological treatments for their panic symptoms over the years, the patients were still enduring anxiety and depressive symptoms ranging from mild to severe, for which reason they had been referred for a full psychiatric re-evaluation. The patients were found to be physically fit, with results of electrocardiogram, full blood count, and kidney, liver and thyroid function tests within normal limits. Their panic symptoms abated within a few weeks following drug treatment using SSRIs, but they remained impaired by persistent background anxiety. In addition to the medication, the patients were advised to engage in a graded programme of aerobic exercise involving swimming or running three times a week, at least 30 minutes each session. Their symptoms resolved within three months after commencing the exercise programme. All patients were eventually discharged from the local psychiatric services.

It seems, therefore, that exercise therapy may be effective in the full panic syndrome, ranging from panic attacks (Broocks et al, 1998; Bandelow et al, 2000) to residual anxiety symptoms (Dratcu, 2001), but this can only be fully confirmed by further research, which can also help to further elucidate exercise's antipanic mode of action. A number of hypotheses have been proposed to explain the effects of exercise therapy in psychiatric disorders in general (Table 2). Although all of them also need further scrutiny, these hypotheses are not mutually exclusive (Daley, 2002). Whether or not any of these mechanisms also plays a part in the therapeutic effects of exercise in panic disorder, aerobic exercise is likely to be advantageous to panic patients for more specific reasons. If it is true that panic patients develop respiratory abnormalities that alter brain functioning and that this, in turn, may perpetuate their panic and anxiety symptoms, performing aerobic exercise regularly is likely to be an acceptable and effective method to dispel this cycle. Aerobic exercise may help panic patients to gradually restore more physiological patterns of breathing, thereby mitigating the adverse effects on brain functioning that may result from chronic hyperventilation (Dratcu, 2000). Residual or persistent symptoms associated with the panic syndrome, which may otherwise not respond to conventional antipanic treatments, may attenuate or resolve as a result.

However, panic disorder also encompasses a psychological dimension (*figure 2*). Catastrophic misinterpretations of bodily sensations (Clark, 1986) and other cognitive distortions have been claimed to be major precipitating factors of panic attacks and anxiety symptoms (Austin and Richards, 2001). An earlier renowned study comparing cognitive therapy, therapeutic doses of imipramine and applied relaxation in the treatment of panic disorder for 15 months reported that cognitive therapy was superior to the other two treatments both in the short and long term, even though imipramine treatment was discontinued after only 6 months (Clark et al, 1994). CBT has since been widely adopted as a treatment for panic disorder (for critical review, see Nadiga et al, 2003) and the current consensus is that the combination of pharmacotherapy and CBT provides the best treatment outcomes (Pollack et al, 2003). Does this mean that the treatment options currently available for panic disorder are enough? Or that physical exercise has nothing special to offer to panic patients, since pharmacotherapy and CBT contain the solutions to all their clinical needs? The answer is a resounding *no* on both counts. First, if either was the case, it would be difficult to justify the apparently unending flow of scientific publications on panic disorder. Second, treatment-refractory panic disorder should be a rare occurrence, but unfortunately this is not true (Corominas et al, 2002; Mathew et al, 2001).

Although these two forms of therapy do not exclude each other, CBT could not be claimed to be superior to exercise therapy in panic disorder before the effectiveness of these two treatments, alone or in combination with pharmacotherapy, is compared in proper randomised controlled trials. There may in fact be reasons to believe that panic patients enroled in programmes of aerobic exercise could do better than those receiving CBT. First, while the ultimate psychological effects of exercise therapy and CBT may prove to be similar (*table 1*), aerobic exercise has the potential to bring about additional therapeutic effects that are beyond the reach of CBT, such as possibly reversing neurophysiological abnormalities associated with the respiratory psychophysiology of panic disorder (*figure 1*). Second, CBT has little impact, if any, on the physical comorbidity that is common in panic patients and which includes cardiovascular problems (Pollack, 2003), whereas physical exercise reduces the risk of coronary heart disease, stroke and obesity-related disorders (Fentem, 1994). Third, exercise therapy may offer several practical advantages over CBT in everyday clinical practice. In the clinical setting, as opposed to the research setting, patients may not always adhere to CBT as it is usually proclaimed. CBT is a relatively complex, formalistic and ascetic method that may not appeal to all tastes, and one that requires guided introspection and a one-to-one relationship with a therapist. In contrast with CBT, exercise can be done in groups, promotes socialisation and contains a built-in component of graded exposure, an automatic benefit to patients with agoraphobia, which is a near-corollary of panic disorder (American Psychiatric Association, 1994). Moreover, compared with the many options of physical exercise available in the community, CBT may not always be widely available or accessible to patients, and it is also likely to be more expensive. Finally, exercise therapy is probably more fun.

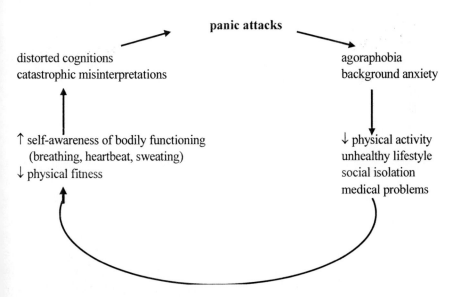

Figure 2. Panic attacks and catastrophic misinterpretation of bodily symptoms. A cognitive model for a self-perpetuating cycle within the pathogenesis of panic disorder.

THE PRACTICALITIES OF PRESCRIBING EXERCISE THERAPY
IN PANIC DISORDER

In reality, of course, there is no competition between exercise therapy and CBT for the treatment of panic disorder, nor between either of these procedures and pharmacotherapy. Far from being mutually exclusive, neurobiological and psychological approaches complement each other as part of any comprehensive model for the pathophysiology of panic disorder and its treatment (*figures 1 and 2*). Nor is exercise therapy a panacea. Not all patients are willing to engage in physical exercise (Mather et al, 2002), and many of those who are may not always adhere to it in the long term (Harland et al, 1999).

At present, exercise therapy should perhaps be seen primarily as an effective adjunctive treatment to pharmacological and psychological treatments of panic disorder. Aerobic exercise is less effective in panic disorder than clomipramine (Broocks et al, 1998), and presumably other antipanic agents as well, and is also likely to have a different mode of action (Broocks et al, 2003). Yet, aerobic exercise may help to resolve persistent residual symptoms in panic patients who have been treated with pharmacotherapy, precisely because it may promote neurophysiological changes that are beyond the reach of these drugs (Dratcu, 2001). Moreover, not only is exercise therapy a form of exposure therapy that concurs with a cognitive-behavioural approach, but the association with psycho-educational methods can boost its benefits (Powell et al, 2001). Exercise therapy can also be considered as an acceptable alternative for panic patients who are unwilling or unable to take medication or pursue psychological treatment (Broocks et al, 1998). Finally, as an adjunctive treatment that is non-pharmacological, non-addictive, and one that has few adverse effects and contraindications, exercise may represent a valuable resource in the clinical management of treatment-refractory panic disorder. Approaches to the management of treatment-refractory panic disorder usually include pharmacological strategies and CBT, but rarely, if ever, exercise therapy (Mathew et al, 2001). Regrettably, exercise therapy has been ignored in the recommendations of the World Council of Anxiety for the treatment of panic disorder (Pollack et al, 2003). However, if it is true that combining pharmacotherapy with CBT provides the best treatment outcomes in panic disorder, the addition of exercise therapy to any such scheme can only enhance therapeutic responses. The same is probably valid for all anxiety disorders other than panic disorder alone.

Programmes of physical exercise for patients with panic or other psychiatric disorders should be flexible and preferably enjoyable, so definite or fixed rules are unlikely to apply. Still, some basic guidelines should be followed:

1. before joining any exercise programme, patients should undergo a full medical examination, which may incorporate tests for cardiorespiratory fitness. Routine investigations, including an electrocardiogram, glucose tolerance test, thyroid function tests, kidney and liver function tests, and a full blood count, are recommended to all patients;
2. professional supervision and exercise counselling are important and should ideally be provided by a trained exercise therapist, at least initially;
3. non-aerobic forms of exercise may also be helpful, but aerobic exercise should be the first choice, particularly in panic disorder, regardless of the modality: running, cycling, swimming, etc;
4. programmes of graded exercise are clearly the best option;
5. regularity is crucial. As a rule of thumb, patients should exercise at least three times a week, at least 30-45 minutes each session. The frequency, intensity and duration of the sessions may increase with time;
6. programmes that last less than one month are probably useless. Exercise therapy should be seen as a long-term activity, which patients should be encouraged to pursue after completion of any treatment protocol;
7. patients' progress should be monitored regularly. As part of the routine, they should be offered the opportunity to discuss their difficulties as well as their successes.

To conclude, it should be noted that, in an age of evidence-based medicine, exercise therapy yields an additional major advantage. Patients do not need to wait either for the outcome of prolonged randomised controlled trials or for the formal approval of official authorities before they receive the treatment. They can simply start to run.

REFERENCES

Abelson, J.L., Weg, J.G., Nesse, R.M., Curtis, G.C. (2001) Persistent respiratory irregularity in patients with panic disorder. *Biological Psychiatry, 49,* 588-595.

Akiyioshi J., Hieda, K., Aoki, Y., Nagayama, H. (2003) Frontal brain hypoactivity as a biological substrate of anxiety in patients with panic disorders. *Neuropsychobiology, 47,* 165-170.

American Psychiatric Association (1994) *Diagnostic and Statistical Manual of Mental Disorders* (4th edition). Washington, DC: American Psychiatric Association.

Angst, J. and Volrath, M. (1991) The natural history of anxiety disorders. *Acta Psychiatrica Scandinavica, 84,* 446-452.

Asmundson, G.J.G. and Stein, M.B. (1994) A preliminary analysis of pulmonary function in panic disorder: Implications for the dyspnea-fear theory. *Journal of Anxiety Disorders*, 8, 63-69.

Austin, D.W. and Richards, J.C. (2001) The catasthrophic misinterpretation model of panic disorder. *Behaviour Research and Therapy*, 39, 1277-1291.

Bandelow, B., Broocks, A., Pekrun, A., George, A., Meyer, T., Pralle, L., Bartmann, U., Hillmer-Vogel U., Ruther, E. (2000) The use of the panic and agoraphobia scale (PandA) in a controlled clinical trial. *Pharmacopsychiatry*, 33, 174-181.

Bass, C. (1987) Panic attacks and hyperventilation. *British Journal of Psychiatry*, 150, 563-564.

Biber, B. and Alkin, T. (1999) Panic disorder subtypes: differential responses to CO_2 challenge. *American Journal of Psychiatry*, 156, 739-744.

Bisaga, A., Katz, J.L., Antonini, A., Wright, C.E., Margouleff, C., Gorman, J.M., Eidelberg, D. (1998) Cerebral glucose metabolism in women with panic disorder. *American Journal of Psychiatry,* 155, 1178-1183.

Borak, J., Sliwinski, P., Piasecki, Z., Zielinski, J. (1991) Psychological status of COPD patients on long term oxygen therapy. *European Respiratory Journal*, 4, 59-62.

Borson, S., McDonald, G.J., Hayle, T, Deffebach, M., Lakshminarayan, S., Van Tuinen, C. (1992) Improvements in mood, physical symptoms and function with nortriptyline for depression in patients with chronic obstructive pulmonary disease. *Psychosomatics*, 33, 190-201.

Breier, A., Charney, D.S., Heninger, G.R. (1986) Agoraphobia with panic attacks: development, diagnostic stability, and course of illness. *Archives of General Psychiatry*, 43, 1029-1036.

Brenes, G.A. (2003) Anxiety and chronic obstructive pulmonary disease: prevalence, impact, and treatment. *Psychosomatic Medicine*, 65, 963-970.

Broocks, A., Meyer, T., Opitz, M., Bartmann, U., Hillmer-Vogel, U., George, A., Pekrun, G., Wedekind, D., Ruther, E., Bandelow, B. (2003) 5-HT$_{1A}$ responsivity in patients with panic disorder before and after treatment with aerobic   exercise,   clomipramine   or   placebo.   *European Neuropsychopharmacology*, 13, 153-164.

Caldirola, D., Bellodi, L., Caumo, A., Migliarese, G., Perna, G. (2004) Approximate entropy of respiratory patterns in panic disorder. *American Journal of Psychiatry*, 161, 79-87.

Caldirola, D., Perna, G., Arancio, C., Bertani, A., Bellodi, L. (1997) The 35% CO_2 challenge test in patients with social phobia. *Psychiatry Research*, 71, 41-48.

Cameron, O.G., Moddell J.G., Haruharan, M. (1990) Caffeine and human cerebral blood flow: a positron emission tomography study. *Life Sciences*, 47, 1141-1146.

Carpiniello, B., Baita, A., Carta, M.G., Sitzia, R., Macciardi, A.M., Murgia, S., Altamura, A.C. (2002) Clinical and psychosocial outcome of patients affected by panic disorder with or without agoraphobia: results from a naturalistic follow-up study. *European Psychiatry*, 17, 394-398.

Carr, D.B. and Sheehan, D.V. (1984) Panic anxiety: a new biological model. *Journal of Clinical Psychiatry*, 45, 323-330.

Carrieri-Kohlman, V., Gormley, J.M., Douglas, M.K., Paul, S.M., Stulbarg, M.S. (1996) Exercise training decreases dyspnea and the distress and anxiety associated with it: monitoring alone may be as effective as coaching. *Chest*, 110, 1526-1535.

Cassano, G.B., Perugi, G., Musetti, L. (1990) Co-morbidity in panic disorder. *Psychiatric Annals*, 20, 517-521.

Clark, D.M. (1986) A cognitive approach to panic. *Behavioural Research and Therapy*, 24, 461-470.

Clark, D. M., Salkovskis, P. M., Hackmann, A., Middleton, H., Anastasiades, P., Gelder, M. (1994) A comparison of cognitive therapy, applied relaxation and imipramine in the treatment of panic disorder. *British Journal of Psychiatry*, 164, 759-769.

Coplan, J.D., Goetz, R., Lein, D.F., Papp. LA., Fyer, A.J., Liebowitz, M.R., Davies, S.O., Gorman, J.M. (1998) Plasma cortisol concentrations preceding lactate-induced panic. Psychological, biochemical and physiological correlates. *Archives of General Psychiatry*, 55, 130-136.

Corominas, A., Guerrero, T., Vallejo, J. (2002) Residual symptoms and comorbidity in panic disorder. *European Psychiatry*, 17, 399-406.

Culpepper, L. (2004) Identifying and treating panic disorder in primary care. *Journal of Clinical Psychiatry,* 65 (suppl 5), 19-23.

Daley, A.J. (2002) Exercise therapy and mental health in clinical populations: is exercise therapy a worthwhile intervention? *Advances in Psychiatric Treatment*, 8, 262-270.

Doyle, A. and Pollack, M.H. (2004) Long-term management of panic disorder. *Journal of Clinical Psychiatry*, 65 (suppl 5), 24-28.

Dratcu, L. (2000). Panic, hyperventilation and perpetuation of anxiety. *Progress in Neuro- Psychopharmacology and Biological Psychiatry*, 24, 1069-1089.

Dratcu, L. (2001) Physical exercise: an adjunctive treatment for panic disorder? *European Psychiatry*, 16, 372-374.

Dratcu, L. and Bond, A. (1998) Panic patients in the non-panic state: physiological and cognitive dysfunction. *European Psychiatry*, 13, 18-25.

Eren, I., Tukel, R., Polat, A., Karaman R., Unal, S. (2003) Evaluation of cerebral blood flow changes in panic disorder with Tc99m-HMPAO SPECT. *Psychiatry Research*, 123, 135-143.

Faulkner, G., Soundy, A.A., Lloyd, K. (2003) Schizophrenia and weight management: a systematic review of interventions to control weight. *Acta Psychiatrica Scandinavica*, 108, 324-332.

Faulkner, G. and Sparkes, A. (1999) Exercise as therapy for schizophrenia. *Journal of Sport and Exercise Psychology*, 21, 52-69.

Fentem, P.H. (1994) Benefits of exercise in health and disease. *British Medical Journal*, 308, 1291-1295.

Fulcher, K.Y. and White, P.D. (1997) Randomised controlled trial of graded exercise in patients with chronic fatigue syndrome. *British Medical Journal*, 314, 1647-52.

Garssen, B., Buikhuisen, M., Van Dyck, R. (1996) Hyperventilation and panic attacks. *American Journal of Psychiatry*, 153, 513-518.

Gary, V. and Guthrie D. (1972) The effects of jogging on physical fitness and self-concept on hospitalized alcoholics. *Quarterly Journal of Studies on Alcohol*, 33, 1073-1078.

Gelder, M.G. (1987) Panic attacks and hyperventilation. *British Journal of Psychiatry*, 150, 564.

Gift, A.G. and Cahill, C.A. (1990) Psychophysiologic aspects of dyspnea in chronic obstructive pulmonary disease: a pilot study. *Heart and Lung*, 19, 252-257.

Goetz, R.R., Klein, D.F., Gorman, J.M. (1996) Symptoms essential to the experience of sodium lactate-induced panic. *Neuropsychopharmacology*, 14, 355-366.

Goodwin, R.D. (2003) The prevalence of panic attacks in the United States: 1980 to 1995. *Journal of Clinical Epidemiology*, 56, 914-916.

Goodwin, R.D. and Eaton, W.W. (2003) Asthma and the risk of panic attacks among adults in the community. *Psychological Medicine*, 33, 879-885.

Goodwin, R.D. and Pine, D.S. (2002) Respiratory disease and panic attacks among adults in the United States. *Chest*, 122, 645-650.

Goodwin, R.D., Pine, D.S., Hoven, C.W. (2003) Asthma and panic attacks among youth in the community. *Journal of Asthma*, 40, 139-145.

Gorman, J.M., Askanazi, J., Liebowitz, M.R., Fryer, A.J., Stein, J., Kinney, J.M., Klein, D.F. (1984) Response to hyperventilation in a group of patients with panic disorder. *American Journal of Psychiatry*, 141, 857-861.

Gorman, J.M., Battista, D., Goetz, R.R., Dillon, D.J., Liebowitz, M.R., Fryer, A.J., Kahn, J.P., Sandberg, D., Klein, D.F. (1989) A comparison of sodium bicarbonate and sodium lactate infusion in the induction of panic attacks. *Archives of General Psychiatry*, 46, 145-150.

Gorman, J.M., Fryer, M.R., Liebowitz, M.R., Klein, D. (1987) Pharmacologic provocation of panic attacks. In: H.Y. Meltzer (Ed.) *Psychopharmacology: The Third Generation of Progress* (pp. 985-993). New York, NY: Raven Press.

Gorman, J.M., Fryer, M.R., Goetz, R., Askanazi, J., Liebowitz, M.R., Fryer, A.J., Kenny, J., Klein, D.F. (1988) Ventilatory physiology of patients with panic disorder. *Archives of General Psychiatry*, 45, 31-19.

Gorman, J.M., Kent, J., Martinez, J., Browne S., Coplan, J., Papp, L.A. (2001) Psysiological changes during carbon dioxide inhalation in patients with panic disorder, major depression, and premenstrual dysphoric disorder: evidence for a central fear mechanism. *Archives of General Psychiatry*, 58, 125-131.

Greene, J.G., Pucino, F., Carlson, J.D., Storsved, M., Strommen, G.L. (1989) Effects of alprazolam on respiratory drive, anxiety and dyspnea in chronic airflow obstruction: a case study. *Pharmacotherapy*, 9, 34-38.

Griez, E., Lousberg, H., Van Der Hout, M.A. (1987) CO_2 vulnerability in panic disorder. *Psychiatry Research, 20,* 87-95.

Griez, E., De Loof, H., Pols, H., Zanbergen, J., Lousberg, H. (1990) Specific sensitivity of patients with panic attacks to carbon dioxide inhalation. *Psychiatry Research, 31,* 193-199.

Grosz, H.J. and Farmer, M. (1969) Blood lactate in the development of anxiety symptoms. *Archives of General Psychiatry, 21,* 611-619.

Hales, R.E. and Travis, T.W. (1987) Exercise as a treatment option for anxiety and depressive disorders. *Military Medicine, 152,* 299-302.

Harland, J., White, M., Drinkwater, C., Chinn, D., Farr, L., Howel, D. (1999) The Newcastle exercise project: a randomised controlled trial of methods to promote physical activity in primary care. *British Medical Journal, 319*, 828-832.

Harrington, P.J., Schmidt, N.B., Telch, M.J. (1996) Prospective evaluation of panic potentiation following 35% CO_2 challenge in non-clinical subjects. *American Journal of Psychiatry, 153*, 823-825.

Kahn, R.S. and Van Praag, H.M. (1992) Panic disorder, a biological perspective. *European Neuropsychopharmacology, 2*, 1-20.

Huffman, J.C. and Pollack, M.H. (2003) Predicting panic disorder among patients with chest pain: an analysis of the literature. *Psychosomatics, 44*, 222-236.

Karajgi, B., Rifkin, A., Doddi, S., Kolli, R. (1990) The prevalence of anxiety disorders in patients with chronic obstructive pulmonary disease. *American Journal of Psychiatry, 147*, 200-201.

Katzman, M.A., Struzik, L., Vijay, N., Coonerty-Femiano, A., Mahamed, S., Duffin, J. (2002) Central and peripheral chemoreflexes in panic disorder. *Psychiatry Research, 113*, 181-192.

Kellner, R., Samet, J., Pathak, D. (1992) Dyspnea, anxiety and depression in chronic respiratory impairment. *General Hospital Psychiatry, 14*, 20-28.

Klein, D.F. (1993) False suffocation alarms, spontaneous panics, and related conditions. *Archives of General Psychiatry, 50*, 306-317.

Klein, D.F. (1996) Panic disorder and agoraphobia: hypothesis. *Journal of Clinical Psychiatry, 57 (suppl. 6)*, 21-27.

Ley, R. (2001) Respiratory psychophysiology and behaviour modification. *Behavior Modification, 25*, 491-494.

Liebowitz, M.R., Fryer, A.J., Gorman, J.M., Levitt, M., Dillon, D., Levy, G., Appleby, I.L., Anderson, S., Palij, M., Davies, S.O., Klein, D.F. (1984) Lactate provocation of panic attacks: I. Clinical and behavioural findings. *Archives of General Psychiatry, 41*, 764-770.

Liebowitz, M.R., Gorman, J.M., Fryer, A.J., Levitt, M., Dillon, D., Levy, G., Appleby, I.L., Anderson, S., Palij, M., Davies, S.O., Klein, D.F. (1985) Lactate provocation of panic attacks: II. Biochemical and physiological findings. *Archives of General Psychiatry, 42*, 709-719.

Lishman, W.A. (1998) *Organic Psychiatry. The psychological consequences of cerebral disorder* (3rd edition). London: Blackwell. pp 507-569.

Lum, L.C. (1987) Hyperventilation syndromes in medicine and psychiatry: a review. *Journal of the Royal Society of Medicine, 80*, 229-231.

Maddock, R.J. and Mateo-Bermudez, J. (1990) Elevated serum lactate following hyperventilation during glucose infusion in panic disorder. *Biological Psychiatry, 27*, 411-418.

Martinez, J.M., Kent, J.M., Coplan, J.D., Browne, S.T., Papp, L.A., Sullivan, G.M., Kleber, M., Perepletchikova, F., Fryer, A.J., Klein, D.F., Gorman, J.M. (2001) Respiratory variability in panic disorder. *Depression and Anxiety, 14,* 232-237.

Martinsen, E. W. (1990) Benefits of exercise for the treatment of depression. *Sports Medicine, 9,* 380-389.

Martinsen, E.W. (1993) Therapeutic implications of exercise for clinically anxious and depressed patients. *International Journal of Sports Psychology, 24,* 185-199.

Martinsen, E.W. (1994) Physical activity and depression: clinical experience. *Acta Psychiatrica Scandinavica, 377,* 23-27.

Martinsen, E.W., Hoffart, A., Solberg, O. (1989). Comparing aerobic with nonaerobic forms of exercise in the treatment of clinical depression: a randomised trial. *Comprehensive Psychiatry, 30,* 324-331.

Mathew, S.J., Coplan, J.D., Gorman, J.M. (2001) Management of treatment-refractory panic disorder. *Psychopharmacology Bulletin, 35,* 97-110.

Meuret, A.E., Wilhelm, F.H., Ritz, T., Roth, W.T. (2003) Breathing training for treating panic disorder. Useful intervention or impediment? *Behavior Modification, 27,* 732-754.

Meuret, A.E., Wilhelm, F.H., Roth, W.T. (2001) Respiratory biofeedback-assisted therapy in panic disorder. *Behavior Modification, 25,* 584-605.

Meuret, A.E., Wilhelm, F.H., Roth, W.T. (2004) Respiratory feedback for treating panic disorder. *Journal of Clinical Psychology, 60,* 197-207.

Mountz, J.M., Modell, J.G, Wilson, M.W., Curtis, G.C., Lee, M.A., Schmaltz, S., Kuhl, D.E (1989) Positron emission tomographic evaluation of cerebral blood flow during state anxiety in simple phobia. *Archives of General Psychiatry, 46,* 1-4.

Nadiga, D.N., Hensley, P.L., Uhlenhuth, E.H. (2003) Review of the long-term effectiveness of cognitive behavioural therapy compared to medications in panic disorder. *Depression and Anxiety, 17,* 58-64.

Nordahl, T.E., Semple, W.E., Gross, M., Mellman, T.A., Stein, M.D., Goyer, P., King, A.C., Uhde, T.W., Cohen, R.M. (1990) Cerebral glucose metabolic differences in patients with panic disorder. *Neuropsychopharmacology, 3,* 261-272.

Nordahl, T.E., Stein, M.B., Benkelfat, C., Semple, W.E., Andreason, P., Zametkin, A., Uhde, T.W., Cohen, R.M. (1998) Regional cerebral metabolic asymmetries replicated in an independent group of patients with panic disorder. *Biological Psychiatry, 44,* 998-1006.

North, T.C., McCullagh, P., Tran, Z.V. (1990) Effects of exercise in depression. *Exercise and Sport Science Reviews, 18,* 379-415.

Nutt, D.J. and Lawson, C. (1992) Panic attacks: a neurochemical overview of models and mechanisms. *British Journal of Psychiatry, 160,* 165-178.

Oakley-Browne, M. (1991) The epidemiology of anxiety disorders. *International Review of Psychiatry, 3,* 243-252.

O'Sullivan, G., Harvey, I., Bass, C., Sheehy, M., Toone, B., Turner, S. (1992) Psychophysiological investigations of patients with unilateral symptoms in the hyperventilation syndrome. *British Journal of Psychiatry, 160,* 664-667.

Papp, L.A., Klein, D.F., Gorman, J.M. (1993a) Carbon dioxide hypersensitivity, hyperventilation and panic disorder. *American Journal of Psychiatry, 150,* 1149-1157.

Papp, L.A., Klein, D.F., Martinez, J., Schneier, F., Cole, R., Liebowitz, M.R., Hollander, E., Fryer, A.J., Jordan, F., Gorman, J.M. (1993b) Diagnostic and substance specificity or carbon-dioxide-induced panic. *American Journal of Psychiatry, 150,* 250-257.

Pelham, T. and Campagna, P. (1991) Benefits of exercise in psychiatric rehabilitation of persons with schizophrenia. *Canadian Journal of Rehabilitation, 4,* 159-168.

Phelan, M., Stradins, L., Morrison, S. (2001) Physical health of people with severe mental illness. Can be improved if primary care and mental health professionals pay attention to it. *British Medical Journal, 322,* 443-444.

Pitts, F.M. and McClure, J.N. (1967) Lactate metabolism in anxiety neurosis. *New England Journal of Medicine, 277,* 1329-1336.

Pollack, M.H., Allgulander, C., Bandelow, B., Cassano, G.B., Greist, J.H., Hollander, E., Nutt, D.J., Okasha, A., Swinson, R.P. (2003) World Council of Anxiety recommendations for the long treatment of panic disorder. *CNS Spectrums, 8 (suppl 1),* 17-30.

Pols, H.J., Hazer, R.C., Meijer, J.A., Verburg, K., Griez, E.J. (1996) Fluvoxamine attenuates panic induced by 35% CO2 challenge. *Journal of Clinical Psychiatry, 57,* 539-542.

Porzelius, J., Vest, M., Nochomovitz, M. (1992) Respiratory function, cognitions and panic in chronic obstructive pulmonary patients. *Behaviour Research Therapy, 30,* 75-77.

Preedy, V.R. and Peters, T. J. (1990) Alcohol and skeletal muscle disease. *Alcohol and Alcoholism, 25,* 177-187.

Rassovsky, Y. and Kushner, M.G. (2003) Carbon dioxide in the study of panic disorder: issues of definition, methodology, and outcome. *Journal of Anxiety Disorders, 17,* 1-32.

Reiman, E.M., Raichle, M.E., Butler, F.K., Herscovitch, P., Robins, E. (1984) A focal brain abnormality in panic disorder, a severe form of anxiety. *Nature,* 310, 683-685.

Reiman, E.M., Raichle, M.E., Robins, E., Butler, F.K., Herscovitch, P., Fox, P., Perlmutter, J. (1986) The application of positron emission tomography to the study of panic disorder. *American Journal of Psychiatry, 143,* 467-477.

Reiman, E.M., Raichle, M.E., Robins, E., Mintun, M.A., Fusselman, M.J., Fox, P.T., Price, J.L., Hackman, K.A. (1989) Neuroanatomical correlates of a lactate-induced anxiety. *Archives of General Psychiatry, 46,* 493-500.

Roy-Byrne, P.P. and Cowley, D. S. (1994/1995) Course and outcome in panic disorder: a review of recent follow-up studies. *Anxiety, 1,* 151-160.

Seier, F.E., Kellner, M., Yassouridis A., Heese, R., Strain, F., Wiedemann, K. (1997) Autonomic reactivity and hormonal secretion in lactate-induced panic attacks. *American Journal of Physiology, 272,* H2630-2638.

Sheehan, D.V. (2002) The management of panic disorder. *Journal of Clinical Psychiatry, 63 (suppl 14),* 17-21.

Shivaram, U., Cash, M., Finch, P.J.P. (1989) Effects of alprazolam on gas exchange, breathing pattern and lung function in COPD patients with anxiety. *Respiratory Care, 34,* 196-200.

Simon, N.M., Safren, S.A., Otto, M.W., Sharma, S.G., Lanka, G.D., Pollack, M.H. (2002) Longitudinal outcome with pharmacotherapy in a naturalistic study of panic disorder. *Journal of Affective Disorders, 69,* 201-208.

Sinha, S., Papp, L.A., Gorman, J.M. (2000) How study of respiratory physiology aided our understanding of abnormal brain function in panic disorder. *Journal of Affective Disorders, 61,* 191-200.

Slaven, L. and Lee, C. (1997) Mood and symptom reporting among middle-aged women: the relationship between menopausal status, hormone replacement therapy, and exercise participation. *Health Psychology, 16,* 203-8.

Smoller, J.W., Pollack, M.H., Otto, M.W., Rosenbaum, J.F., Kradin, R.L. (1996) Panic anxiety, dyspnea and respiratory disease. Theoretical and clinical considerations. *American Journal of Respiratory and Critical Care Medicine, 154,* 6-17.

Smoller, J.W., Pollack, M.H., Systrom, D., Kradin, R.L. (1998) Sertraline effects on dyspnea in patients with obstructive airways disease. *Psychosomatics, 39,* 24-29.

Stahl, S.M. (2002) The metabolic syndrome: psychopharmacologists should weigh the evidence of weighing the patient. *Journal of Clinical Psychiatry, 63,* 1094-1095.

Swoboda, H., Amering M, Windhaber J, Katschnig H (2003) The long-term course of panic disorder: an 11 year follow-up. *Journal of Anxiety Disorders, 17*, 223-232.

Veale, D., LeFevre, K., Pantelis, C., de Souza, V., Mann, A., Sargeant, A. (1992) Aerobic exercise in the adjunctive treatment of depression: a randomized controlled trial. *Journal of the Royal Society of Medicine, 85*, 541-544.

Verburg, K., Pols, H., De Leeuw, M., Griez, E. (1998) Reliability of the 35% carbon dioxide panic provocation. *Psychiatry Research, 78*, 207-214.

Welkowitz, L.A., Papp, L., Martinez, J., Browne, S., Gorman, J.M. (1999) Instructional set and physiological response to CO2 inhalation. *American Journal of Psychiatry, 156*, 745-8.

Wilhelm, F.H., Gerlach, A.L., Roth, W.T. (2001a) Slow recovery from voluntary hyperventilation in panic disorder. *Psychosomatic Medicine, 63*, 638-649.

Wilhelm, F.H., Trabert, W., Roth, W.T. (2001b) Physiologic instability in panic disorder and generalized anxiety disorder. *Biological Psychiatry, 49*, 596-605.

Wilhelm, F.H., Trabert, W., Roth, W.T. (2001c) Characteristics of sighing in panic disorder. *Biological Psychiatry, 49*, 606-614.

Wittchen, H.U. and Essau, C.A. (1993) Epidemiology of panic disorder: progress and unresolved issues. *Journal of Psychiatric Research, 27 (suppl.1)*, 47-68.

Wulsin, L., Liu, T., Storrow, A., Evans, S., Dewan, N., Hamilton, C. (2002) A randomized, controlled trial of panic disorder treatment initiation in an emergency department chest pain center. *Annals of Emergency Medicine, 39*, 139-143.

Yellowlees, P.M., Alpers, J.H., Bowden, J.J., Bryant, G.D., Ruffin, R.E. (1987) Psychiatric morbidity in patients with chronic airflow obstruction. *Medical Journal of Australia, 146*, 305-307.

Yeragani, V.K., Rao, R., Tancer, M., Uhde, T. (2004) Paroxetine decreases respiratory irregularity and nonlinear measures of respiration in patients with panic disorder. *Neuropsychobiology, 49*, 53-57.

Yonkers, K.A., Buce, S.E., Dyck, I.R., Keller, M.B. (2003) Chronicity, relapse, and illness course of panic disorder, social phobia, and generalized anxiety disorder: findings in men and women from 8 years of follow-up. *Depression and Anxiety, 17*, 173-179.

In: Exercise and Health Research   ISBN: 978-1-60021-985-6
Editor: M. D. Johansen, pp. 71-98   © 2008 Nova Science Publishers, Inc.

Chapter 3

STRESS-REACTIVITY AND HEALTH: THE IMPACT OF EXERCISE AND NUTRITION

Mark Hamer[1] and Stephen H. Boutcher[2]

[1]Unilever Health Institute, Unilever Research Vlaardingen,
Vlaardingen, The Netherlands
[2]School of Medical Sciences, Faculty of Medicine, University of New South
Wales, Sydney, Australia

ABSTRACT

Psychological stress is a common aspect of modern day living and can be experienced in multiple forms that produce differing cardiovascular and immune responses. Heightened psychophysiological reactivity has been linked to unfavourable health outcomes that include cardiovascular disease, hypertension, diabetes, and sub-clinical infections. The relationship between stress-reactivity and health seems to be moderated and mediated by a number of factors such as lifestyle and genetics. One common aspect of modern living is physical inactivity and the consumption of highly refined foods lacking in essential nutrients. The purpose of this review is to highlight the role of stress-reactivity in the development of ill-health and outline the potential beneficial impact of exercise and various nutrients on the physiological response to stress, with suggestions for future directions of research. There is growing evidence supporting the stress-reactivity lowering effects of exercise and specific nutrients. These effects appear to be important for the maintenance of health in a stressful modern day environment. Although evidence pertaining to the clinical relevance of these stress-reactivity lowering effects is currently lacking, exercise and nutritional intervention should be recommended for lowering hyper-reactive responses to psychological stress.

Keywords: psychological stress; stress hormones; cardiovascular reactivity; immune reactivity; exercise; functional food nutrients

INTRODUCTION

The effect of psychological stress on health is becoming a serious concern. Figures from the World Health Organisation show that stress related disorders affect nearly 450 million people worldwide [1]. US health authorities estimate that 19 million Americans suffer from anxiety disorders [2] and half a million people in Great Britain believe that work-related stress is making them ill [3]. Thus, scientific interest in the area of stress and health has increased substantially and public health bodies are becoming increasingly aware of stress-related health problems (see, for example, the recently published British Heart Foundation booklet entitled 'Stress and your heart'[4]). Stress is a common aspect of the modern day lifestyle and although a certain degree of stress is beneficial to stimulate mental and physical performance, the inability to cope with stress may be detrimental. The relatively recent emergence of stress-related ill-health may in part be explained by the gene-by-environment interaction model of stress reactivity for essential hypertension development [5]. This model suggests that the stress response may become a health risk only in conjunction with a genetic predisposition or with additional potentiating environmental factors. The emergence of a modern day lifestyle that is characterised by increasing levels of habitual physical inactivity and the consumption of highly refined foods, which are lacking in essential nutrients, may partially explain why stress-related health problems are emerging as one of the major epidemics of the new millennium. Therefore, there is now considerable interest within the scientific community, public health bodies, and health conscious individuals to control or reduce the impact of stress on health. The current recommendations for coping with stress include exercising, healthy eating, reducing alcohol intake, smoking, and drugs, using time and stress management, and getting support from friends [4].

The purpose of this chapter is to highlight the role of stress-reactivity in the development of ill-health and outline the potential beneficial impact of exercise and various nutrients on the physiological response to stressors with suggestions for future directions of research. The term 'stress-reactivity' that is used throughout this chapter is defined as the physiological response to an acute psychological stress task that is represented as a change score (for example, blood pressure reactivity can be calculated as blood pressure during the stress task minus baseline blood pressure).

IMMUNE REACTIVITY

Acute Stress

Acute stress stimulates immune function, which results in increases in delayed type hypersensitivity (DTH) response, natural killer cell activity (NKCA), CD8+ cell number, pro-inflammatory cytokines, type 1 (Th1) cytokines (IL-2, IFN-γ) and mucosal immunoglobins (Ig) [6]. Cortisol release during acute stress is thought to shift the balance away from Th1 driven cell mediated responses toward Th2 driven anti-body mediated responses. This shift may increase susceptibility to certain infections. Cacioppo et al. [7] have demonstrated that high cardiac and hypothalamic-pituitary-adrenal (HPA) reactivity in response to a stress task (6-min mental arithmetic / 6-min speech task) predicted immuno-suppression to latent Epstein-Barr Virus (EBV). Cohen et al [8] demonstrated that subjects showing greater cortisol reactivity to a simulated public speaking task (2-min preparation followed by a 3-min video taped speech delivery) had increased risk of verified upper respiratory tract infection (URTI) but only when they reported high negative life events. Further cross-sectional analysis demonstrated that subjects showing smaller immune responses (NKCA and CD8+ cell reactivity) to the speech task had increased risk of self reported URTI during high stress weeks. However, of the 51 subjects meeting the self reported criteria for URTI, only 30 actually went to the clinic for verification resulting in using self-reported URTI that may reflect bias in reporting of illness. In another recent study, Kunz-Ebrecht et al [9] reported that both high and low cortisol stress reactivity has potentially adverse effects because they found an inverse relationship between interleukin-6 (IL-6) release and cortisol reactivity. The higher cortisol reactors, who reported greater impaired mental health, may be at risk from suppressed immune function, whereas low cortisol response and excessive IL-6 release may initiate a chronic inflammatory state (see section below). Collectively, these studies show that individual stress reactivity may be useful to predict those individuals most susceptible to infection.

Chronic Stress Exposure

Epidemiological studies have demonstrated that forms of chronic stress (family conflict and stressful life events) are correlated with increased incidence of serologically verified URTIs [8, 10-12]. Early virus-challenge studies, in which subjects were exposed to a cold or influenza virus and assessed for stress levels using stressful life events or emotional distress scales, provided mixed support for a relationship between chronic stress and impaired immune response [13,14]. However, more recently studies have provided evidence to indicate that chronically stressed individuals (for example, elderly care-givers) demonstrate a suppressed secondary immune response to vaccination [15-18]. Also, in a recently published study Miller et al [19] demonstrated that healthy, young adults with higher levels of self-reported cumulative daily stress levels in the 10 days following influenza vaccination had significantly reduced antibody responses compared with lower-stress subjects. Furthermore, chronic stress is generally ascribed to the suppression of other immune markers such as reduced DTH response, NKCA, CD4+ and CD8+ cells, lymphocyte proliferation response, and type 1 cytokines.

In summary, up-regulation of the immune system in response to acute stress may be viewed as a normal adaptation to psychological challenge, whereas repeated episodes of acute stress (chronic stress) may be associated with more serious impairment of immune function that may have implications for ill-health. However, it is also likely that chronic stress influences the immune responsiveness to acute stress [20,21].

Inflammatory Responses and Disease

An integral part of the initial immune response involves the release of pro-inflammatory cytokines, such as IL-6 and tumor necrosis factor-α (TNF-α) that regulate the production of acute-phase proteins such as C-reactive protein (CRP). As already discussed, this inflammatory response is induced by psychological stress that is most likely related to activation of the major stress-related hormones. It has, therefore, been suggested that repeated episodes of acute psychological stress may induce a chronic inflammatory process culminating in insulin resistance, non-insulin dependent diabetes, metabolic syndrome X, and atherosclerosis [22,23]. Indeed, both IL-6 and CRP are associated with increased mortality risk [24] and higher CRP is an independent risk factor for metabolic syndrome [25], cardiovascular events [26,27], and hypertension [28,29].

CARDIOVASCULAR REACTIVITY

Acute Stress

The basis of the cardiovascular response to stress is an increase in blood pressure (BP) that is tightly regulated by cardiac and/or systemic hemodynamic changes, depending on the type and duration of the psychological task. This response is thought to be largely driven by the sympathetic nervous system (SNS) that can be observed by measuring the changes in sympathetic nerve activity, catecholamine release, and autonomic balance during and after stress. A standard laboratory stressor, such as the Stroop colour-word task, may result in a heart rate (HR) increase of 10-15 bpm and an increase in mean arterial BP of 10-15 mmHg. The hemodynamic responses are, however, more complex. For example, forearm skeletal muscle blood flow may increase up to 100% in response to the Stroop task [30], whereas blood flow to the kidney may be significantly reduced [31,32]. Other hemodynamic systems are also activated during stress. For example, a number of studies have examined the effects of an acute stress task on endothelial function by measuring flow-mediated vasodilatation (FMD) [33-37]. Ghiadoni et al [36] used a 3 min mental stress task with healthy subjects and showed that FMD was reduced by 50% for 90 mins following the task and only returned to normal after 4 hrs in comparison with a time-control, non-stress condition. This reduction in endothelial dependent FMD following acute stress was comparable to those results associated with chronic endothelial dysfunction in diabetic subjects. These findings, which demonstrate stress-induced transient endothelial dysfunction, were recently replicated by others using a variety of stress tasks in healthy subjects [33,34]. In contrast, Harris et al [37] showed that mental stress enhanced the FMD response by 64% in healthy subjects and Lind et al [35] observed a stress-induced reduction in FMD only when normalised for the degree of hyperaemic blood flow. The reasons for these discrepancies are unclear but the most convincing results appear to be from Ghiadoni et al [36] who used a time-control, non-stress condition. A further important aspect of the endothelium during the stress response is in the release of endothelin-1 [38,39]. Endothelin-1 is a potent vasoconstrictor peptide that is released basolaterally by endothelial cells and elicits smooth muscle cell constriction.

Changes in several hemostatic factors including platelet activation (platelet factor 4 and β-thromboglobulin), increased hematocrit, and total plasma protein in response to laboratory stress tasks have also been demonstrated [40]. The disturbance of endothelial function and hemostatic factors may play a key role in stress related cardiovascular disease pathways that will be discussed below.

Chronic Stress Exposure

The proposed relationship between heightened reactivity and disease probably manifests itself through exposure to repeated episodes of acute stress. Heightened cardiovascular reactivity has been linked to a number of unfavourable health outcomes that include the prediction of cardiovascular disease [41] and hypertension [42]. Most recently, systolic and diastolic BP reactivity to a laboratory-based psychological task in 990 subjects was shown to significantly predict the 5 yr upward drift in systolic and diastolic BP, accounting for 3.6% and 2.9% of the variance, respectively [43].

There are a number of potential mechanisms that have been associated with the relationship between heightened reactivity and disease. These mechanisms are based on the damaging effects of excessive release of stress hormones and biomechanical stimuli in the endothelium due to pulsatile blood flow and changes in the shear forces imposed by blood flow under increased pressure. For example, at specific sites that are most exposed to changes in blood flow (increased turbulence and changes in shear stress) researchers have found atheromatous plaques in primate models of chronic stress [44,45] and in human athersclerotic disease [23]. Endothelial dysfunction plays a key role in the initiation of atherosclerosis because nitric oxide (NO) production from healthy endothelial cells has an anti-atherogenic effect by inhibiting cellular adhesion, migration, and proliferation responses [46,47]. This may be exacerbated by stress-induced increases in platelet aggregability that is associated with coronary artery occlusion and/or constriction. Thus, the impact of stress on endothelium dependent vascular homeostasis may play a critical role in the development of cardiovascular disease.

A further important factor is that the catecholamines demonstrate trophic properties at physiological levels that enhances the growth of vascular smooth muscle [48-50]. This effect has been demonstrated in humans when acute stress induced rapid rises in serum mitogenic activity for vascular smooth muscle cells

[51,52]. This may play a significant role in a vascular remodeling process that has been linked to the development of hypertension [53].

THE STRESS RESPONSE AND EXERCISE

Exercise and Immune Reactivity

There is emerging evidence to suggest that regular aerobic exercise of moderate intensity can have benefits on immune related health. For example, the antibody response to influenza vaccine was enhanced in elderly active subjects (those participating in greater than 20 min exercise three or more times per week) compared with their moderately active or inactive counterparts [54]. Also, elderly exercisers demonstrated normal CD4:CD8 ratio, increased NK-cell concentration, and less decline in phagocytic activity of neutrophils in comparison with their sedentary counterparts [55]. Furthermore, a number of large scale cross-sectional studies have found an inverse relationship between CRP and fitness/ physical activity level after adjustment for age, body mass index, medication, inflammatory disease, diabetes, and smoking habits [56-58]. A 9 month longitudinal training study with 14 subjects also observed significant reductions in CRP [59]. There appears to be limited research that has examined the effects of exercise and immune stress-reactivity. A prospective study demonstrated that sedentary teenage girls had elevated levels of self-reported illness during times of high stress in comparison with their physically active counterparts [60]. Also, LaPerriere et al [61] performed a longitudinal study to examine the effect of 5 weeks exercise training in buffering immune changes in response to the stress of a seropositive diagnosis in an AIDS risk group. They found that subjects in the control group demonstrated declines in circulating NK cells whilst no changes were observed for the experimental group. In contrast, Moyna et al [62] conducted a cross-sectional study to examine the relation between aerobic fitness and immune responses (cell counts, NKCA, lymphocyte proliferation) to an acute psychological stress task in healthy young males but found no effect of fitness level. The null findings of this latter study may have been a result of low statistical power (with an n of 15 per group) because there is a high individual variation for immune measures such as NKCA. Given the limited depth of immune function measures that have been examined in previous research there is much scope for further work in this area. For example, there is some evidence from animal research to suggest 4 wks of voluntary physical activity prior to a psychological stressor in rats (inescapable tail-shock stress) reduces the stress-induced depression of anti-KLH IgM and IgG_{2a} antibodies by blunting the sympathetic response [63]. There is also evidence from non-exercise interventions demonstrating effects for improving the response to vaccination. For example, using a mindfulness meditation intervention, that was applied in the work environment for 8wks, boosted humoral immune responses to an influenza vaccination in 25 healthy subjects compared with a wait listed control group [64]. Therefore, there is a need for more research that examines the efficacy of exercise interventions for improving immune function in stressed populations. These studies should especially focus on measures that provide greater insight into immune function, such as clinical endpoints and response to vaccination. Furthermore, studies should address the impact of exercise interventions on stress-induced inflammatory responses that have been linked to metabolic disorders and CVD.

Exercise and Cardiovascular Reactivity

A meta-analysis by Crews and Landers [65] provided evidence to suggest that fitness level, acute, and chronic exercise may be related to a stress reactivity lowering mechanism. They reported that greater fitness and exercise was associated with a reduced cardiovascular response to psychological stressors, with a moderate overall effect size of 0.42 for systolic BP, 0.40 for diastolic BP, and 0.39 for HR using 13 and 17, and 30 studies respectively. A further calculation was made to compare the mean effect size from 9 acute and 25 chronic exercise studies, collapsing effect sizes across a number of psycho-physiological variables, which produced mean effect sizes of 0.11 and 0.59 respectively. There is also strong evidence to demonstrate a BP stress-reactivity lowering effect following a bout of acute exercise [66-71] and from a 12 month exercise training study [72].

SNS Modulation

One of the exercise- reactivity lowering mechanisms may be closely related to reductions in SNS activation following aerobic exercise training [73,74]. Boutcher et al [75] reported that trained males exhibited a greater phasic decrease in respiratory sinus arrhythmia (parasympathetic withdrawal), compared to untrained, during the Stroop task. This suggests that trained individuals possibly have a lower activation of the SNS during stress, and show a greater reliance on the parasympathetic system that is beneficial for health. Aerobic exercise training programmes lasting for 2 wks [76], 6 wks [77], and 6 months [78] also appear to enhance indices of parasympathetic modulation at rest, although the effect of an exercise training intervention on autonomic control during stress appears to be undetermined. Reductions in catecholamine reactivity to stress tasks following an acute bout of exercise have also been consistently demonstrated. For example, Peronnet et al. [79] demonstrated a 56% reduction in plasma epinephrine reactivity to the Stroop task following a 2-hr bout of moderate intensity exercise. Also, Brownley et al. [66] demonstrated 91 and 61% reductions in epinephrine and norepinephrine reactivity, respectively, to a speech stress task after a 25-min bout of moderate intensity exercise. Furthermore, Brownley et al [66] showed that the reduced norepinephrine reactivity was the best single predictor of post-exercise reduced BP reactivity (significantly decreased SBP, DBP, and MAP reactivity of 8.8mmHg, 7.7mmHg, 4.3mmHg respectively) accounting for 46%, 31%, and 24% of the variance in SBP, DBP, and MAP reactivity, respectively. However, the observed reductions in catecholamine reactivity should be interpreted with caution given that the experimental design (pre and post exercise stress task) is vulnerable to task habituation.

Adrenergic Modulation

In the same study [66] β-adrenergic receptor responsiveness was assessed before and after exercise using a β-adrenergic agonist (isoproterenol) to determine the dose required to elicit a HR increase of 25 bpm (chronotropic dose:CD_{25}) and a peripheral vascular resistance decrease of 50% (vasodilatory dose: VD_{50}). The results showed significant increases in post-exercise β1- and β2- receptor responsiveness evidenced by reductions in CD_{25} and VD_{50} throughout the 2 hr post-exercise period. These findings suggest that the BP response to stress was primarily blunted by enhancing β2-mediated vasodilatation. However, one limitation of this study is that isoproterenol infusions were not conducted in the presence of vagal blockade. Thus, it is not clear to what extent agonist induced compensatory parasympathetic withdrawal may have influenced the findings.

Further adrenergic mechanisms may be related to a blunting of α-adrenergic mediated vasoconstriction in areas such as the kidney, which are vulnerable to stress-induced vasoconstriction . However, Halliwill et al [80] recently showed that vascular responsiveness to α1- and α2-agonists was maintained during a 60-min post-exercise hypotension period in humans. Nevertheless, other mechanisms may operate such as pre-synaptic inhibition by neuropeptide Y that may reduce norepinephrine release, although such studies have not yet been performed.

Opioidergic Inhibition

β-endorphin, which is produced during exercise and has stress modulatory characteristics, has also been suggested to play a potential role in the post-exercise reduction in BP-reactivity. McCubbin et al [81-83] have shown that the opiate antagonist naloxone increases BP responses to psychological stress. Also, McCubbin et al [84] showed that the lower BP reactivity observed in aerobically trained compared with untrained males was abolished after treatment with an opiate antagonist, suggesting a role for opioidergic inhibition of cardiovascular stress reactivity.

Hemodynamics and Endothelial Function

An important area that appears to have gained limited attention is the effect of exercise on the hemodynamic response to stress. We have shown that in offspring hypertensives, who demonstrate an exaggerated forearm skeletal muscle vasodilatation response to the Stroop mental challenge, those that are aerobically trained appear to have a significantly reduced response compared with their untrained counterparts [30]. We have also demonstrated a significant reduction in forearm blood flow reactivity to the Stroop task after an acute bout of exercise in offspring of hypertensives (unpublished data). However, there does not appear to be any work that has examined the effect of exercise on transient endothelial dysfunction that is observed following acute stress. Studies have shown that regular aerobic exercise prevents and restores age-related declines in endothelium-dependent vasodilatation in elderly men [85,86], and enhances endothelial function in young men [87]. Given that sympathetic activation may be involved with a reduction in endothelium dependent vasodilatation [88] it is plausible that exercise could reduce or eliminate stress-induced endothelial dysfunction. Furthermore, reductions in SNS activation following acute or chronic exercise may potentially have a beneficial effect on hemostatic responses and mitogenic activity in relation to acute episodes of stress.

In summary, there is substantial evidence to support a role for exercise as an intervention to reduce hyper-reactive responses to stress. Further work is required to substantiate these effects with regards to immune health and vascular function.

THE STRESS RESPONSE AND NUTRITION

Immune Modulation

There are a limited number of placebo controlled intervention trials that have examined the effect of nutritional supplementation on stress-induced immune suppression. Shenkin et al [89] performed a placebo controlled trial to examine the influence of 12 weeks of micronutrient supplementation on the immune response to examination stress in 171 medical students. Although there were significant differences in cytokine production (IL-6, TNF-α) between stressed and non-stressed subjects, the supplement had no effect on immune outcome. Several other nutrients, such as aged garlic, ginseng root saponins, ginsenosides, and ocimum santum seed oil, have been identified from animal studies as playing a potential role in ameliorating stress-induced immune suppression [90-92].

HPA Axis Modulation

From a neurochemical viewpoint, the best coping strategies to alleviate stress and mood deterioration would result in increased activity of relevant serotonergic and opioid mediated pathways, which may be achieved by high carbohydrate/ low protein consumption. High carbohydrate/ low protein meals, which raise the plasma ratio of tryptophan, have been demonstrated to produce anti-depressant effects in clinical populations [93]. Furthermore, increases in brain serotonin appear to modulate adreno-cortical reactivity probably through alterations in 5-HT1a and 5-HT2 receptor sites located at the hypothalamic and pituitary brain area [94]. Markus et al [95,96] performed two dietary intervention studies that were designed to increase the plasma tryptophan - large neutral amino acid ratio (Trp-LNAA), thereby enhancing brain serotonergic activity. In the first study Markus et al. [95] increased the plasma Trp-LNAA by 42% in subjects administered a high carbohydrate/ low protein meal compared to those given a high protein / low carbohydrate meal. This significantly reduced the cortisol response to a laboratory stress task in subjects highly prone to stress, although the HR response was unaffected by the intervention. In the next study [96], administration of a dietary protein enriched in tryptophan (α-lactalbumin) had a similar effect, which increased plasma Trp-LNAA by 48% and reduced cortisol responses to a laboratory stressor in a double-blind placebo controlled trial with 58 subjects. However, these results were less convincing due to the large difference in baseline cortisol level between control and experimental conditions. The serotonin-stress hypothesis appears to be highly complex because different serotonergic pathways appear to initiate as well as terminate the adrenocorticol axis [97] that possibly explains why baseline cortisol level was elevated during the α-lactalbumin intervention period. Some further work relating to milk proteins and stress management has been conducted by a French dairy ingredients company who have recently revealed a milk casein hydrolysate (Lactium®) that is claimed to deliver stress relieving benefits and is backed by five clinical trials on 190 healthy volunteers. Although detailed information on these trials is not currently available, a number of stress markers appear to have been measured including cardiovascular, digestive, emotional, and social parameters.

Jezova et al [98] performed a parallel, randomized, double blind, placebo-controlled trial in 70 healthy subjects (33 male, 37 female) to examine the effect of a single dose (120 mg) of Ginkgo biloba on BP and cortisol responses to a combined mental and physical stressor. The stressor consisted of a memory test followed immediately by two 3-min bouts of static handgrip exercise at 30% of maximum voluntary contraction. The experimental group demonstrated a significant reduction in SBP and DBP response (of approximately 10 mmHg) but not HR during the combined stressor, and cortisol was significantly reduced post-stress only in males. That the BP response was comparatively large (30 mmHg increase in control group) compared to a standard response for a mental challenge alone suggests that the handgrip exercise was predominantly responsible for this response. Therefore, the data is difficult to interpret given that the mechanisms for BP responses to isometric exercise are different compared with the response to mental challenge alone. However, data from a number of animal studies has also demonstrated reductions in stress-induced corticosterone release following chronic oral administration of Ginkgo biloba [99-101]. The mechanism is thought to be inhibition of adrenal cortical peripheral-type benzodiazepine receptors (PBR). Amri et al [102,103] have demonstrated that in vivo treatment of rats with ginkgolide B resulted in 80% reduction of adrenocorticotropic hormone (ACTH)-stimulated corticosterone production by adrenocortical cells and later demonstrated transcriptional suppression of the PBR gene. PBR also appear to be upregulated after acute stress in humans [104] that was measured in vivo using a platelet binding assay.

Adrenergic/Endothelial Modulation

Brody et al [105] conducted a parallel, double-blind placebo controlled trial in 120 healthy subjects to examine the effect of a high dosage ascorbic acid supplement (3 g/day, 14 days) on BP and cortisol response to a public speaking and mental arithmetic stress task. The subjects performed the stress task only once following the intervention period to avoid habituation effects. Compared with the placebo group, the ascorbic acid group demonstrated significantly reduced SBP (-8.3 mmHg) and DBP (-5 mmHg) reactivity during the first minute of the task and significantly lower BP throughout the 40-min stress period. Also, the ascorbic acid group demonstrated significantly faster salivary cortisol response, but no differences in cortisol reactivity. There were no differences in the placebo and ascorbic acid groups for the cortisol response to low-dose ACTH provocation, which excludes the possibility that adrenal responsiveness was modified. Instead, possible mechanisms may include modulation of noradrenergic activity and improvement of endothelial dependent vasodilatation by the ascorbic acid supplement. For example, in a series of well controlled infusion trials Lembo et al [106] demonstrated that in hypertensives, compared with controls, the vascular hyper-responsiveness to norepinephrine is eliminated after arterial infusion of ascorbic acid. Also, they showed that the vascular hyper-responsiveness was due to an impairment of nitric oxide activity that was corrected by infusion of ascorbic acid. They provided further evidence to suggest nitric oxide activity could be impaired through norepinephrine-induced oxygen free radical production, thus suggesting that the effect of ascorbic acid may be linked to scavenger action on oxygen free radicals. The efficacy of ascorbic acid in relation to improved endothelial function and nitric oxide activity in humans has also been demonstrated in a number of other high quality publications [107-109].

Fish oil supplementation is another possible candidate for lowering the stress response through adrenergic modulation. Fish oils contain essential omega-3 fatty acids in the form of eicosapentaenoic acid (EPA) and docosahexaenoic acid (DHA) that have been associated with a significant reduction in cardiovascular events in patients with coronary heart disease [110]. Two human trials have been conducted to examine the efficacy of fish oil supplementation for lowering the stress response. Sawazaki et al [111] conducted a randomised, double-blind placebo controlled trial in 14 healthy volunteers to examine the effect of fish oil consumption on plasma catecholamine and cortisol responses to a chronic stress period. The volunteers were administered capsules containing either 1.5g DHA/day or placebo containing mixed plant oil during a 9wk examination period that consisted of 20 stressful medical exams. Although there was no difference in epinephrine levels between groups at the beginning or end of the supplementation period, norepinephrine levels were significantly reduced in the DHA group only. However, rather surprisingly, cortisol levels were significantly reduced in the placebo group and not the DHA group following the intervention. In contrast, Delarue et al [112] showed that plasma epinephrine and cortisol responses to a 30-min stress task, consisting of mental arithmetic and Stroop tasks, was significantly blunted after 3wks of fish oil supplementation (1.1g/d EPA, 0.7g/d DHA) compared with the control response in 7 healthy subjects. Despite the apparently reduced activation of the adrenal gland by the fish oil intervention, BP and HR responses to the stress task were unaffected. However, it should be noted that this trial was not placebo controlled and no attempt was made to control for the effects of task habituation that severely weakens the findings from this study. Data from animal studies supports the efficacy of DHA supplementation for reducing the norepinephrine response to stress. Rousseau et al [113] subjected rats to an intermittent feeding schedule to induce stress for 8 wks, administering a semi-purified diet containing either 10% sunflower seed oil or a mixture of sunflower seed oil and DHA. The stressed rats fed with the control diet demonstrated a significantly greater increase in cardiac norepinephrine levels following the stress period in comparison with the stressed DHA group. Also, the stressed control rats had a significantly elevated heart rate compared with stressed rats given the DHA diet and unstressed controls. However, the norepinephrine data is slightly difficult to interpret because unstressed rats that were supplemented with DHA appeared to have significantly higher levels of cardiac norepinephrine compared with the unstressed control group that suggests stress induced changes may have differed between groups due to differences in baseline norepinephrine. The mechanisms that have been associated with the CVD risk lowering benefits of fish oil supplementation include decreased risk of arrhythmias, decreased risk of thrombosis, decreased triglycerides and remnant lipoprotein levels, decreased rate of atherosclerotic plaque growth, improved endothelial function, lowered BP, and reduced inflammatory responses [110]. Although current evidence for the stress reactivity lowering effects of fish oil supplementation remains equivocal, future trials should attempt to investigate whether any of the aforementioned mechanisms may be involved.

Lastly, two more trials have been conducted to examine the efficacy of herbal interventions for lowering cardiovascular responses to the Stroop mental stress task. Facchinetti et al [114] examined the effect of supplementation with ginseng root extract (*Eleutherococcus senticosus*, unspecified dose taken for 30 days) in a randomized placebo controlled trial. The authors claimed that treatment with the ginseng extract reduced HR response to the Stroop task by approximately 40%

although closer inspection of the data suggests that the effects are due to habituation to the task because the placebo group also demonstrated marked reductions in reactivity to the post treatment Stroop task. In a non-placebo controlled trial a standard dose of kava (n=18) or valerian (n=18) was administered for 7 days in healthy subjects [115]. Significant reductions in the systolic BP response to the stress task were observed in comparison with the baseline stress response, whilst the control group (n=18) remained unchanged. Further reductions in HR-reactivity were observed for the valerian group and both intervention groups demonstrated reductions in perceived pressure during the task.

Cholesterol Lowering

A further area of interest may be to focus on the reduction of stress-reactivity through cholesterol lowering dietary interventions. Minami et al [116] demonstrated that hypercholesterolemia patients have higher BP responses to a stress task compared with normal cholesterolemic controls. Furthermore, Sung et al [117] demonstrated a significant reduction (-8 mmHg) in the systolic BP response to a mental arithmetic task after a reduction in total cholesterol of 26% in patients with high cholesterol following treatment with Lovastatin in a 6 week double-blind cross-over design. The authors suggested that the mechanism may be related to improved nitric oxide mediated vasodilatation during stress resulting in a greater vasodilatation response, although unfortunately systemic hemodynamic responses were not assessed.

Dietary Amplifiers

Various dietary amplifiers of cardiovascular reactivity are also known to exist that include salt [118] and caffeine [119]. Miller et al [118] studied the effect of sodium loading and parental history of hypertension on the cardiovascular response to stress. In offspring hypertensives sodium loading elevated total peripheral resistance and norepinephrine response to stress relative to placebo conditions and compared with controls. In a double blind placebo controlled trial Lane et al [119] showed that 500mg caffeine administration amplified the increases in BP and HR associated with higher levels of perceived stress during the working day.

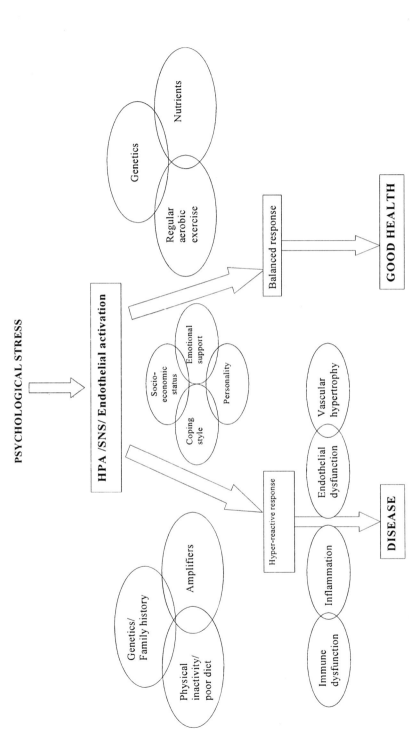

Figure 1. Stress pathways involved with the development of disease and the impact of various lifestyle factors.

In summary, there appears to be a limited number of well-controlled studies that have examined the efficacy of nutritional intervention for lowering the response to stress in humans. An inherent problem with the area of 'functional foods' research is that most nutrients, if administered at normal levels to healthy subjects, appear to only have subtle effects. Thus, it sometimes may be of more use to examine the emotional aspects (mood and anxiety) of nutritional intervention for alleviating the stress response. Nevertheless, an important aspect of future research will be to identify the key nutrients, commonly found in the everyday diet, that can alleviate unfavourable systemic hemodynamic responses to stress. For example, the high levels of flavonoids, catechins, tannins, and other polyphenolic compounds present in some vegetables, fruits, soy, tea, and red wine that are believed to induce NO formation from the endothelium [120] could potentially also play a role in maintaining homeostasis during periods of stress. The consumption of black tea (900 mL daily for 4 wks), for example, was shown to improve endothelium dependent vasodilatation in patients with coronary artery disease in a randomised placebo controlled trial [121].

CONCLUSION

Heightened physiological responses to psychological stress appear to contribute to disease pathways. Presently, the most compelling evidence in relation to non-pharmacological strategies for reducing the stress response comes from the exercise literature. The data consistently shows that an acute bout of moderate intensity exercise prior to a laboratory stress task reduces SBP reactivity to the task by approximately 10 mmHg compared with control conditions. A limited number of nutritional intervention studies have also demonstrated some promising stress-reactivity lowering effects in humans. For example, in well-designed trials supplementation with different herbal extracts, milk proteins, vitamin C, and fish oils have demonstrated some stress-reactivity lowering effects.

That immune, cardiovascular, and endocrine reactivity to stress appear to be inter-correlated and stable within individuals suggests that these responses form a unified stress response [122,123]. The mechanisms associated with stress-reactivity lowering effects can almost exclusively be linked to the SNS, the HPA axis, and the endothelium. Therefore interventions for reducing the acute response to stress should be primarily targeted at these systems (Figure 1). Specific mechanisms that appear to be important for maintaining a balanced stress response are related to norepinephrine release and/or α-adrenergic receptor responsiveness, β2-adrenergic receptor responsiveness, HPA axis feedback mechanisms, and preservation of endothelial homeostasis (related to nitric oxide and endothelin release).

Future human trials that examine the efficacy of interventions for lowering the acute stress response should be mindful of a number of factors. Firstly, laboratory stress tasks are highly vulnerable to habituation. Therefore, it is critical to design trials where subjects are minimally exposed to the same task with a control group to demonstrate no task habituation or alternatively employ a parallel design where subjects from experimental and control groups are only exposed to the task once following the intervention. Secondly, the stress response can be highly variable between individuals although stable within a person. Therefore, it is important to screen subjects in order to select those with the highest stress response ("high reactors") because it is in these individuals that the intervention is likely to be most affective. Thirdly, the reactivity model is multi-factorial and additional mediating variables such as socio-economic status, life events and social support, family history of hypertension and CVD, and emotional/ coping style should not be ignored when examining the effects of exercise and/or nutrition on the stress response. Ideally they should be included as covariates in any statistical analysis. It is feasible that lifestyle interventions may reduce stress-reactivity by moderating some of these mediating factors.

Lastly, it is unethical to experimentally induce severe chronic stress in human subjects, which unfortunately considerably weakens the experimental design of human chronic stress studies and therefore makes it difficult to imply causation. Therefore, the most important issues in this field of research are to demonstrate clear causal pathways between stress and disease and to uncover the clinical relevance of the stress-reactivity buffering effects of exercise and nutrition. Future research should also examine whether exercise and nutrition can provide a robust stress buffering effect for naturally occurring stressors and the dose-response relationships.

REFERENCES

[1]   The World Health Report (WHO): *Mental health – new understanding, new hope*. 2001.

[2]   National Institute of Health (US): *Anxiety disorders*. 1994.

[3]   Health & Safety Executive (UK): *Self-reported work related illness in 2001/02 – results from a household survey*. 2002.

[4]   British Heart Foundation: *Stress and your heart*. 2004.

[5]   Light KC: Hypertension and the reactivity hypothesis: the next generation. *Psychosom Med* 63:744-746, 2001.

[6]   Herbert TB, Cohen S: Stress and immunity in humans: a meta-analytic review. *Psychosom.Med* 55(4): 364-379, 1993.

[7]   Cacioppo JT, Berntson GG, Malarkey WB, Kiecolt-Glaser JK, Sheridan JF, Poehlmann KM, Burleson MH, Ernst JM, Hawkley LC, Glaser R: Autonomic, neuroendocrine, and immune responses to psychological stress: the reactivity hypothesis. *Ann N.Y. Acad Sci* 840:664-673., 1998.

[8]   Cohen S, Hamrick N, Rodriguez MS, Feldman PJ, Rabin BS, Manuck SB: Reactivity and vulnerability to stress-associated risk for upper respiratory illness. *Psychosom Med* 64: 302-310, 2002.

[9]   Kunz-Ebrecht SR, Mohamed-Ali V, Feldman PJ, Kirschbaum C, Steptoe A: Cortisol responses to mild psychological stress are inversely associated with proinflammatory cytokines. *Brain Behav Immunol* 17: 373-383, 2003.

[10]   Cobb JM, Steptoe A: Psychosocial stress and susceptibility to upper respiratory tract illness in an adult population sample. *Psychosom Med* 58(5): 404-412, 1996.

[11]   Clover RD, Abell T, Becker LA, Crawford S, Ramsey CN, Jr: Family functioning and stress as predictors of influenza B infection. *J Fam Pract* 28(5):535-539, 1989.

[12]   Graham NM, Douglas RM, Ryan P: Stress and acute respiratory infection. *Am J Epidemiol* 124(3): 389-401, 1986.

[13]   Totman R, Kiff J, Reed SE, Craig JW: Predicting experimental colds in volunteers from different measures of recent life stress. *J Psychosom.Res* 24(3-4): 155-163, 1980.

[14]   Broadbent DE, Broadbent MH, Phillpotts RJ, Wallace J: Some further studies on the prediction of experimental colds in volunteers by psychological factors. *J Psychosom Res* 28(6):511-523, 1984.

[15]   Kiecolt-Glaser JK, Glaser R, Gravenstein S, Malarkey WB, Sheridan J: Chronic stress alters the immune response to influenza virus vaccine in older adults. *Proc Natl Acad Sci U.S.A*, 93(7): 3043-3047, 1996.

[16]   Glaser R, Kiecolt-Glaser JK, Malarkey WB, Sheridan JF: The influence of psychological stress on the immune response to vaccines. *Ann N.Y. Acad Sci* 840:649-655, 1998.

[17]   Vedhara K, Cox NK, Wilcock GK, Perks P, Hunt M, Anderson S, Lightman S L, Shanks NM: (1999). Chronic stress in elderly carers of dementia patients and antibody response to influenza vaccination. *Lancet* 353(9153): 627-631, 1999.

[18] Burns VE, Carroll D, Ring C, Harrison LK, Drayson M: Stress, coping, and hepatitis B antibody status. *Psychosom Med* 64(2): 287-293, 2002.

[19] Miller GE, Cohen S, Pressman S, Barkin A, Rabin BS, Treanor JJ: Psychological stress and antibody response to influenza vaccination: when is the critical period for stress, and how does it get inside the body? *Psychosom Med.* 66(2):215-23, 2004.

[20] Benschop RJ, Brosschot JF, Godaert GLR, De Smet MBM, Geenen R, Olff M, Heijnen CJ, Ballieux RE: Chronic stress effects immunologic but not cardiovascular responsiveness to acte psychological stress in humans. *Am. J. Physiol.* 266: R75-80, 1994.

[21] Pike JL, Smith TL, Hauger RL, Nicassio PM, Patterson TL, McClintick J, Costlo C, Irwin MR. Chronic life stress alters sympathetic, neuroendocrine, and immune responsivity to an acute psychological stressor in humans. *Psychosom. Med.* 59: 447-457, 1997.

[22] Black PH: The inflammatory response is an integral part of the stress response: Implications for atherosclerosis, insulin resistance, type II diabetes and metabolic syndrome X. *Brain Behav Immun.* 17:350-64, 2003.

[23] Black PH, Garbutt LD: Stress, inflammation and cardiovascular disease. *J Psychosom Res.* 52:1-23, 2002.

[24] Taaffe DR, Harris TB, Ferrucci L, Rowe J, Seeman TE: Cross-sectional and prospective relationships of interleukin-6 and C-reactive protein with physical performance in elderly persons: MacArthur studies of successful aging. *J Gerontol A Biol Sci Med Sci* 55:M709-15, 2000.

[25] Heald AH, Anderson SG, Ivison F, Laing I, Gibson JM, Cruickshank K: C-reactive protein and the insulin-like growth factor (ICF)-system in relation to risk of cardiovascular disease in different ethnic groups. *Atherosclerosis* 170:79-86, 2003.

[26] Thompson SG, Kienast J, Pyke SDM, Haverkate F, van de Loo JCW: Hemostatic factors and the risk of myocardinal infarction or sudden death in patients with angina pectoris. *New Eng J Med* 332: 635-41, 1995.

[27] Ridker PM, Hennekens CH, Buring JE, Rifai N. C-reactive protein and other markers of inflammation in the prediction of cardiovascular disease in women. *New Eng J Med* 342:836-43, 2000.

[28] Bautista LE, Lopez-Jaramillo P, Vera LM, Casas JP, Otero AP, Guaracao AI. Is C-reactive protein an independent risk factor for essential hypertension? *J Hypertens.* 19(5):857-61, 2001.

[29] Sung KC, Suh JY, Kim BS, Kang JH, Kim H, Lee MH, Park JR, Kim SW. High sensitivity C-reactive protein as an independent risk factor for essential hypertension. *Am J Hypertens.* 16(6):429-33, 2003.

[30] Hamer M, Boutcher Y, Boutcher SH. Cardiovascular and renal responses to mental challenge in highly and moderately active males with a family history of hypertension. *J Hum Hypertens*. 16:319-26, 2002.

[31] Hollenburg NK, Williams GH, Adams DF: Essential hypertension: abnormal renal vascular and endocrine responses to a mild psychological stimulus. *Hypertension* 3:11-17, 1981.

[32] van Hooft IM, Grobbee DE, Derkx FH, de Leeuw PW, Schalekamp MA, Hofman A. Renal hemodynamics and the renin-angiotensin-aldosterone system in normotensive subjects with hypertensive and normotensive parents. *N Engl J Med*. 324:1305-11, 1991.

[33] Gottdiener JS, Kop WJ, Hausner E, McCeney MK, Herrington D, Krantz DS. Effects of mental stress on flow-mediated brachial arterial dilation and influence of behavioral factors and hypercholesterolemia in subjects without cardiovascular disease. *Am J Cardiol*. 92(6):687-91, 2003.

[34] Spieker LE, Hurlimann D, Ruschitzka F, Corti R, Enseleit F, Shaw S, Hayoz D, Deanfield JE, Luscher TF, Noll G. Mental stress induces prolonged endothelial dysfunction via endothelin-A receptors. *Circulation* 105(24):2817-20, 2002.

[35] Lind L, Johansson K, Hall J. The effects of mental stress and the cold pressure test on flow-mediated vasodilation. *Blood Press*. 11(1):22-7, 2002.

[36] Ghiadoni L, Donald AE, Cropley M, Mullen MJ, Oakley G, Taylor M, O'Connor G, Betteridge J, Klein N, Steptoe A, Deanfield JE. Mental stress induces transient endothelial dysfunction in humans. *Circulation*. 102(20): 2473-8, 2000.

[37] Harris CW, Edwards JL, Baruch A, Riley WA, Pusser BE, Rejeski WJ, Herrington DM. Effects of mental stress on brachial artery flow-mediated vasodilation in healthy normal individuals. *Am Heart J*. 139(3):405-11, 2000.

[38] Treiber FA, Kapuku GK, Davis H, Pollock JS, Pollock DM. Plasma endothelin-1 release during acute stress: role of ethnicity and sex. *Psychosom Med*. 64(5):707-13, 2002.

[39] Noll G, Wenzel RR, Schneider M, Oesch V, Binggeli C, Shaw S, Weidmann P, Luscher TF. Increased activation of sympathetic nervous system and endothelin by mental stress in normotensive offspring of hypertensive parents. *Circulation*. 93(5):866-9, 1996.

[40] Patterson SM, Krantz DS, Gottdiener JS, Hecht G, Vargot S, Goldstein DS. Prothrombotic effects of environmental stress: changes in platelet function, hematocrit, and total plasma protein. *Psychosom Med*. 57(6): 592-9, 1995.

[41] Krantz DS, Manuck SB: Acute psychophysiologic reactivity and risk of cardiovascular disease: a review and methodological critique. *Psychol. Bull.* 96:435-464, 1984.

[42] Matthews KA, Wood KL, Allen MT: Cardiovascular reactivity to stress predicts future blood pressure status. *Hyperten.* 22:479-485, 1993.

[43] Carroll D, Ring C, Hunt K, Ford G, Macintyre S. Blood pressure reactions to stress and the prediction of future blood pressure: effects of sex, age, and socioeconomic position. *Psychosom Med.* 65:1058-64, 2003.

[44] Kaplan JR, Pettersson K, Manuck SB, Olsson G. Role of sympathoadrenal medullary activation in the initiation and progression of atherosclerosis. *Circulation.* 84 Suppl:VI23-32, 1991.

[45] Manuck SB, Adams MR, McCaffery JM, Kaplan JR: Behaviorally elicited heart rate reactivity and atherosclerosis in ovariectomized cynomolgus monkeys. *Arterioscler Thromb Vasc Biol* 17:1774-9, 2000.

[46] Ross R: Atherosclerosis--an inflammatory disease. *N Engl J Med.* 340(2): 115-26, 1999.

[47] Lüscher TF, Vanhoutte PM: The Endothelium: Modulator of cardiovascular function. Boca Raton, Fla: *CRC Press*; 1990: 1-215.

[48] Yamori Y, Igawa T, Kanbe T, Kihara M, Nara Y, Horie R. Mechanisms of structural vascular changes in genetic hypertension: analyses on cultured vascular smooth muscle cells from spontaneously hypertensive rats. *Clin Sci* (Lond). 61 Suppl 7:121s-123s, 1981.

[49] Blaes N, Boissel JP: Growth-stimulating effect of catecholamines on rat aortic smooth muscle cells in culture. *J Cell Physiol.* 116:167-72, 1983,

[50] Yu SM, Tsai SY, Guh JH, Ko FN, Teng CM, Ou JT. Mechanism of catecholamine-induced proliferation of vascular smooth muscle cells. *Circulation* 94(3):547-54, 1996.

[51] Gutstein WH, Teresi JA, Wu JM, Ramirez M, Salimian F, Cui Y, Paul I, Jabr S. Increased serum mitogenic activity for arterial smooth muscle cells associated with relaxation and low educational level in human subjects with high but not low hostility traits: implications for atherogenesis. *J Psychosom Res.* 46(1):51-61, 1999.

[52] Cui Y, Gutstein WH, Jabr S, Hsieh TC, Wu JM. Control of human vascular smooth muscle cell proliferation by sera derived from 'experimentally stressed' individuals. *Oncol Rep.* 5(6):1471-4, 1998.

[53] Folkow B: Structural factor in primary and secondary hypertension. *Hypertension.* 16:89-101,1990.

[54] Kohut ML, Cooper MM, Nickolaus MS, Russell DR, Cunnick JE: Exercise and psychosocial factors modulate immunity to influenza vaccine in elderly individuals. *J Gerontol A Biol Sci Med Sci.* 57:M557-62, 2002.

[55] Yan H, Kuroiwa A, Tanaka H, Shindo M, Kiyonaga A, Nagayama A. Effect of moderate exercise on immune senescence in men. *Eur J Appl Physiol.* 86:105-11, 2001.

[56] Church TS, Barlow CE, Earnest CP, Kampert JB, Priest EL, Blair SN. Associations between cardiorespiratory fitness and C-reactive protein in men. *Arterioscler Thromb Vasc Biol.* 22:1869-76, 2002.

[57] Ford ES: Does exercise reduce inflammation? Physical activity and C-reactive protein among U.S. adults. *Epidemiology.* 13:561-8, 2002.

[58] Abramson JL, Vaccarino V. Relationship between physical activity and inflammation among apparently healthy middle-aged and older US adults. *Arch Intern Med.* 162:1286-92, 2002.

[59] Mattusch F, Dufaux B, Heine O, Mertens I, Rost R. Reduction of the plasma concentration of C-reactive protein following nine months of endurance training. *Int J Sports Med.* 21:21-4, 2000.

[60] Brown JD, Siegel JM: Exercise as a buffer of life stress: a prospective study of adolescent health. *Health Psychol.* 7:341-53, 1988.

[61] LaPerriere AR, Antoni MH, Schneiderman N, Ironson G, Klimas N, Caralis P, Fletcher MA: Exercise intervention attenuates emotional distress and natural killer cell decrements following notification of positive serologic status for HIV-1. *Biofeedback Self Regul.* 15:229-42, 1990.

[62] Moyna NM, Bodnar JD, Goldberg HR, Shurin MS, Robertson RJ, Rabin BS: Relation between aerobic fitness level and stress induced alterations in neuroendocrine and immune function. *Int J Sports Med.* 20:136-41, 1999.

[63] Fleshner M: Exercise and neuroendocrine regulation of antibody production: protective effect of physical activity on stress-induced suppression of the specific antibody response. *Int J Sports Med.* 21 Suppl 1:S14-9, 2000.

[64] Davidson RJ, Kabat-Zinn J, Schumacher J, Rosenkranz M, Muller D, Santorelli SF, Urbanowski F, Harrington A, Bonus K, Sheridan JF. Alterations in brain and immune function produced by mindfulness meditation. *Psychosom Med.* 65(4):564-70, 2003.

[65] Crews DJ, Landers DM: A meta-analytic review of aerobic fitness and reactivity to psychosocial stressors. *Med. Sci. Sports Exerc.* 19: S114-S120, 1987.

[66] Brownley KA, Hinderlitter AL, West SG, Girdler SS, Sherwood A, Light KA: Sympathoadrenergic mechanisms in reduced hemodynamic stress responses after exercise. *Med. Sci. Sports Exerc.* 35: 978-986, 2003.

[67] West SG, Brownley KA, Light KC: Post-exercise vasodilatation reduces diastolic blood pressure responses to stress. *Ann. Behav. Med.* 20:77-83, 1998.

[68] Probst M, Bulbulian R, Knapp C. Hemodynamic responses to the Stroop and cold pressor tests after submaximal cycling exercise in normotensive males. *Physiol. & Behav.* 62:1283-1290, 1997.

[69] Rejeski JW, Thompson A, Brubaker PH, Miller HS: Acute exercise: Buffering psychosocial stress responses in women. *Health Psych.* 11: 355-362, 1992.

[70] Roy M, Steptoe A: The inhibition of cardiovascular responses to mental stress following aerobic exercise. *Psychophysiol.* 28: 689-700, 1991.

[71] Steptoe A, Kearsley N, Walters N: Cardiovascular activity during mental stress following vigorous exercise in sportsmen and inactive men. *Psychophysiol.* 30:245-252, 1993.

[72] King AC, Baumann K, O'Sullivan P, Wilcox S, Castro C. Effects of moderate-intensity exercise on physiological, behavioral, and emotional responses to family caregiving: a randomized controlled trial. *J Gerontol A Biol Sci Med Sci.* 57:M26-36, 2002.

[73] Duncan JJ, Farr JE, Upton SJ, Hagan RD, Oglesby ME, Blair SN. The effects of aerobic exercise on plasma catecholamines and blood pressure in patients with mild essential hypertension. *JAMA.* 254:2609-13, 1985.

[74] Jennings G, Nelson L, Nestel P, Esler M, Korner P, Burton D, Bazelmans J. The effects of changes in physical activity on major cardiovascular risk factors, hemodynamics, sympathetic function, and glucose utilization in man: a controlled study of four levels of activity. *Circulation.* 73:30-40, 1986.

[75] Boutcher SH, Nugent FW, McLaren PF, Weltman AL: Heart period variability of trained and untrained men at rest and during mental challenge. *Psychophysiol.* 35:16-22, 1998.

[76] Lee CM, Wood RH, Welsch MA. Influence of short-term endurance exercise training on heart rate variability. *Med Sci Sports Exerc.* 35:961-9, 2003.

[77] Yamamoto K, Miyachi M, Saitoh T, Yoshioka A, Onodera S. Effects of endurance training on resting and post-exercise cardiac autonomic control. *Med Sci Sports Exerc.* 33:1496-502, 2001.

[78] Levy WC, Cerqueira MD, Harp GD, Johannessen KA, Abrass IB, Schwartz RS, Stratton JR. Effect of endurance exercise training on heart rate variability at rest in healthy young and older men. *Am J Cardiol.* 82:1236-41, 1998.

[79] Perronet FD, Massicotte D, Paquet J, Brisson G, De Champlain J: Blood pressure and plasma catecholamine responses to various challenges during exercise recovery in man. *Eur. J. Appl. Physiol.* 58:551-555, 1989.

[80] Halliwill JR, Dinenno FA, Dietz NM: Alpha-adrenergic vascular responsiveness during postexercise hypotension in humans. *J Physiol.* 550(Pt 1):279-86, 2003.

[81] McCubbin JA, Surwit RS, Williams RB Jr. Endogenous opiate peptides, stress reactivity, and risk for hypertension. *Hypertension.* 7(5):808-11, 1985.

[82] McCubbin JA, Surwit RS, Williams RB Jr. Opioid dysfunction and risk for hypertension: naloxone and blood pressure responses during different types of stress. *Psychosom Med.* 50(1):8-14, 1988.

[83] McCubbin JA, Bruehl S, Wilson JF, Sherman JJ, Norton JA, Colclough G. Endogenous opioids inhibit ambulatory blood pressure during naturally occurring stress. *Psychosom Med.* 60(2):227-31, 1998.

[84] McCubbin JA, Cheung R, Montgomery TB, Bulbulian R, Wilson JF. Aerobic fitness and opioidergic inhibition of cardiovascular stress reactivity. *Psychophysiology.* 29(6):687-97, 1992.

[85] DeSouza CA, Shapiro LF, Clevenger CM, Dinenno FA, Monahan KD, Tanaka H, Seals DR. Regular aerobic exercise prevents and restores age-related declines in endothelium-dependent vasodilation in healthy men. *Circulation.* 102(12): 1351-7, 2000.

[86] Jensen-Urstad K, Bouvier F, Jensen-Urstad M. Preserved vascular reactivity in elderly male athletes. *Scand J Med Sci Sports.* 9(2): 88-91, 1999.

[87] Clarkson P, Montgomery HE, Mullen MJ, Donald AE, Powe AJ, Bull T, Jubb M, World M, Deanfield JE. Exercise training enhances endothelial function in young men. *J Am Coll Cardiol.* 33(5): 1379-85, 1999.

[88] Hijmering ML, Stroes ES, Olijhoek J, Hutten BA, Blankestijn PJ, Rabelink TJ. Sympathetic activation markedly reduces endothelium-dependent, flow-mediated vasodilation. *J Am Coll Cardiol.* 39(4): 683-8, 2002.

[89] Shenkin A, Salmon P, Taylor S, Taylor W, Byrne SM, Barnes RMR, Taxman B. Micronutrient supplementation and the immune response to examination stress [abstract]. *Brain Behav Immunol* 17: 205, 2003.

[90] Kyo E, Uda N, Ushijima M, Kasuga S, Itakura Y. Prevention of psychological stress-induced immune suppression by aged garlic extract. *Phytomed* 6:325-330, 1999.

[91] Yun-Man L, Xiu-Juan G, Wen-Xue Y. Effects of ginseng root saponins and ginsenosides Rb1 on immunity in cold water swim stress mice and rats. *Acta Pharma Sinica* 14: 401-404, 1993.

[92] Mediratta PK, Sharma KK, Singh S. Evaluation of immunomodulatory potential of Ocimum sanctum seed oil and its possible mechanism of action. *J Ethnopharmacol* 80:15-20, 2002.

[93] Rosenthal NE, Genhart MJ, Caballero B, Jacobsen FM, Skwerer RG, Coursey RD, Rogers S, Spring BJ: Psychobiological effects of carbohydrate- and protein-rich meals in patients with seasonal affective disorder and normal controls. *Biol Psych* 25 (8): 1029-1040, 1989.

[94] Maes M, Meltzer H: *The serotonin hypothesis of major depression.* In: "Psychopharmacology: the fourth generation of progress". New York: Raven, pp 933-944, 1995.

[95] Markus R, Panhuysen G, Tuiten A, Koppeschaar H: Effects of food on cortisol and mood in vulnerable subjects under controllable and uncontrollable stress. *Physiol Behav* 70:333- 342, 2000.

[96] Markus CR, Olivier B, Panhuysen GE, Van Der Gugten J, Alles MS, Tuiten A, Westenberg HG, Fekkes D, Koppeschaar HF, de Haan EE: The bovine protein alpha-lactalbumin increases the plasma ratio of tryptophan to the other large neutral amino acids, and in vulnerable subjects raises brain serotonin activity, reduces cortisol concentration, and improves mood under stress. *Am J Clin Nutr* 71 (6):1536-1544, 2000.

[97] Graeff FG, Guimaraes FS, De Andrade TG, Deakin JF. Role of 5-HT in stress, anxiety, and depression. *Pharmacol Biochem Behav.* 54(1):129-41, 1996.

[98] Jezova D, Duncko R, Lassanova M, Kriska M, Moncek F.Reduction of rise in blood pressure and cortisol release during stress by Ginkgo biloba extract (EGb 761) in healthy volunteers. *J Physiol Pharmacol.* 53(3):337-48, 2002.

[99] Rai D, Bhatia G, Sen T, Palit G. Anti-stress effects of Ginkgo biloba and Panax ginseng: a comparative study. *J Pharmacol Sci.* 93(4):458-64, 2003.

[100] Rapin JR, Lamproglou I, Drieu K, DeFeudis FV. Demonstration of the "anti-stress" activity of an extract of Ginkgo biloba (EGb 761) using a discrimination learning task. *Gen Pharmacol.* 25(5):1009-16, 1994.

[101] Markus CR, Lammers JH. Effects of Ginkgo biloba on corticosterone stress responses after inescapable shock exposure in the rat. *Pharmacol Biochem Behav.* 76(3-4):487-92, 2003.

[102] Amri H, Drieu K, Papadopoulos V. Transcriptional suppression of the adrenal cortical peripheral-type benzodiazepine receptor gene and inhibition of steroid synthesis by ginkgolide B. *Biochem Pharmacol.* 65(5):717-29, 2003.

[103] Amri H, Drieu K, Papadopoulos V. Ex vivo regulation of adrenal cortical cell steroid and protein synthesis, in response to adrenocorticotropic hormone stimulation, by the Ginkgo biloba extract EGb 761 and isolated ginkgolide B. *Endocrinology.* 138(12):5415-26, 1997.

[104] Gavish M, Katz Y, Bar-Ami S, Weizman R. Biochemical, physiological, and pathological aspects of the peripheral benzodiazepine receptor. *J Neurochem.* 58(5):1589-601, 1992.

[105] Brody S, Preut R, Schommer K, Schurmeyer TH. A randomized controlled trial of high dose ascorbic acid for reduction of blood pressure, cortisol, and subjective responses to psychological stress. *Psychopharmacology* (Berl). 159(3):319-24, 2002.

[106] Lembo G, Vecchione C, Izzo R, Fratta L, Fontana D, Marino G, Pilato G, Trimarco B. Noradrenergic vascular hyper-responsiveness in human hypertension is dependent on oxygen free radical impairment of nitric oxide activity. *Circulation.* 102(5):552-7, 2000.

[107] Taddei S, Virdis A, Ghiadoni L, Magagna A, Salvetti A. Vitamin C improves endothelium-dependent vasodilation by restoring nitric oxide activity in essential hypertension. *Circulation.* 97(22):2222-9, 1998.

[108] Levine GN, Frei B, Koulouris SN, Gerhard MD, Keaney JF Jr, Vita JA. Ascorbic acid reverses endothelial vasomotor dysfunction in patients with coronary artery disease. *Circulation.* 93(6):1107-13, 1996.

[109] Solzbach U, Hornig B, Jeserich M, Just H. Vitamin C improves endothelial dysfunction of epicardial coronary arteries in hypertensive patients. *Circulation.* 96(5):1513-9, 1997.

[110] Kris-Etherton PM, Harris WS, Appel LJ. Omega-3 fatty acids and cardiovascular disease: new recommendations from the American Heart Association. *Arterioscler Thromb Vasc Biol.* 23(2):151-2, 2003.

[111] Sawazaki S, Hamazaki T, Yazawa K, Kobayashi M. The effect of docosahexaenoic acid on plasma catecholamine concentrations and glucose tolerance during long-lasting psychological stress: a double-blind placebo-controlled study. *J Nutr Sci Vitaminol* (Tokyo) 45(5):655-65, 1999.

[112] Delarue J, Matzinger O, Binnert C, Schneiter P, Chiolero R, Tappy L. Fish oil prevents the adrenal activation elicited by mental stress in healthy men. *Diabetes Metab.* 29(3):289-95, 2003.

[113] Rousseau D, Moreau D, Raederstorff D, Sergiel JP, Rupp H, Muggli R, Grynberg A. Is a dietary n-3 fatty acid supplement able to influence the cardiac effect of the psychological stress? *Mol Cell Biochem.* 178(1-2):353-66, 1998.

[114] Facchinetti F, Neri I, Tarabusi M. Eleutherococcus senticosus reduces cardiovascular stress response in healthy subjects: a randomized, placebo-controlled trial. *Stress & Health* 18: 11-17, 2002.

[115] Cropley M, Cave Z, Ellis J, Middleton RW. Effect of kava and valerian on human physiological and psychological responses to mental stress assessed under laboratory conditions. *Phytother Res.* 16(1):23-27, 2002.

[116] Minami M, Atarashi K, Ishiyama A, Hirata Y, Goto A, Omata M. Pressor hyperreactivity to mental and hand grip stressors in patients with hyper-cholesterolemia. *J Hypertens.* 17(2):185-192, 1999.

[117] Sung BH, Izzo JL Jr, Wilson MF. Effects of cholesterol reduction on BP response to mental stress in patients with high cholesterol. *Am J Hypertens.* 10(6):592-9, 1997.

[118] Miller SB, Friese M, Sita A. Parental history of hypertension, sodium loading, and cardiovascular response to stress. *Psychosom Med.* 57:381-9, 1995.

[119] Lane JD, Pieper CF, Phillips-Bute BG, Bryant JE, Kuhn CM. Caffeine affects cardiovascular and neuroendocrine activation at work and home. *Psychosom Med.* 64:595-603, 2002.

[120] Achike FI, Kwan CY. Nitric oxide, human diseases and the herbal products that affect the nitric oxide signalling pathway. *Clin Exp Pharmacol Physiol.* 30:605-15, 2003.

[121] Duffy SJ, Keaney JF Jr, Holbrook M, Gokce N, Swerdloff PL, Frei B, Vita JA. Short- and long-term black tea consumption reverses endothelial dysfunction in patients with coronary artery disease. *Circulation.* 104(2):151-6, 2001.

[122] Cohen S, Hamrick N, Rodriguez MS, Feldman PJ, Rabin BS, Manuck SB. The stability of and intercorrelations among cardiovascular, immune, endocrine, and psychological reactivity. *Ann Behav Med.* 22:171-9, 2000.

[123] Cohen S, Hamrick N. Stable individual differences in physiological response to stressors: implications for stress-elicited changes in immune related health. *Brain Behav Immun.* 17:407-14, 2003.

In: Exercise and Health Research
Editor: M. D. Johansen, pp. 99-122

ISBN: 978-1-60021-985-6
© 2008 Nova Science Publishers, Inc.

Chapter 4

THERAPEUTIC LIFESTYLE CHANGE TO REDUCE METABOLIC SYNDROME: FOCUS ON EXERCISE

David Alexander Leaf[*],
Departments of Medicine, Greater Los Angeles V.A. Healthcare System
U.C.L.A. School of Medicine, Los Angeles, California, USA

Ronald W. Deitrick,
Department of Exercise Science
University of Scranton, Scranton, Pennsylvania 18510, USA

Nancy D. Harada
UCLA Schools of Medicine and Public Health
Geriatric Research, Education & Clinical Center
VA Greater Los Angeles Healthcare System,
11301 Wilshire Blvd., Los Angeles, California 90073, USA

---

* Address correspondence to: David Alexander Leaf M.D., M.P.H.; Division of General Internal Medicine, 111G, Greater Los Angeles V.A. Healthcare System, 11301 Wilshire Blvd., Los Angeles, California, 90073; Tel (310) 268-3254; FAX (310) 268-4933; E-mail: David.Leaf@med.va.gov

ABSTRACT

Background

During the past two decades, Metabolic Syndrome (MetS) in the U.S. has increased to the point of being 'epidemic', primarily due to the increased prevalence of obesity. MetS is associated with increased coronary artery disease (CAD) risk. Although dietary interventions are a fundamental component of therapeutic lifestyle change (TLC) programs aimed at weight reduction, physical activity and exercise play a pivotal in reinforcing and sustaining long-term weight loss.

Methods

This article reviews and describes MetS including approaches for implementing physical activity in the context of TLC interventions. These include center- and phone-based programs as well as provider-based intervention settings.

Results and Conclusions

While TLC interventions aimed at reducing MetS are a public imperative, the most effective intervention remains to be elucidated. The various approaches used can be described as effective and having common characteristics. Further research is needed to determine the best method for reducing the risk of MetS.

Keywords: Physical activity, obesity, lifestyle, cardiovascular disease risk, insulin resistance

Over the past two decades, the prevalence of the Metabolic Syndrome (MetS) in the US has progressively increased to the point that it is now regarded as 'epidemic'. [1] This trend is primarily due to the increasing prevalence of obesity, which is up 74% since 1991. According to the latest National Health and Nutrition Examination Survey (NHANES), an estimated 131 million American adults are overweight or obese. [2] The prevalence of MetS increases among aging and sedentary individuals. [3,4,5]

Table 1. NCEPT MetS Criteria*

1. Abdominal obesity (waist circumference > 102 cm [40 inches] in men, > 88 cm [35 inches] in women).
2. Triglycerides ≥ 150 mg/dL
3. Plasma high-density lipoprotein (HDL)-cholesterol < 40 mg/dL in men, < 50 mg/dL in women.
4. Blood pressure elevation (≥130/≥85 mm Hg [or receiving anti-hypertensive therapy]).
5. Fasting plasma glucose > 110 mg/dL.

* Three or more of the above conditions must be present.

MetS is defined as having 3 or more of the following conditions: 1. Abdominal obesity (waist circumference > 102 cm [40 inches] in men, > 88 cm [35 inches] in women); 2. Triglycerides ≥ 150 mg/dL; 3. Plasma high-density lipoprotein (HDL)-cholesterol < 40 mg/dL in men, < 50 mg/dL in women; 4. Blood pressure elevation (≥130/≥85 mm Hg [or receiving anti-hypertensive therapy]); 5. Fasting plasma glucose > 110 mg/dL. [6] This definition has recently been validated [7] and is summarized in Table 1.

MetS is associated with increased CAD risk. [8-14] A recent analysis of 6,447 men with CAD enrolled in the West of Scotland Coronary Prevention Study (WSCOP) showed the presence of MetS at baseline predicted CAD events (Hazard Ratio = 1.30 [1.00 to 1.67]) in a multivariate model incorporating conventional CAD risk factors. [8] Men with 4 or 5 features of MetS had a 3.7-fold increased risk for CAD events than those with none. In another study, Wong et al. [14] have shown that controlling blood pressure and lipid-related CAD risk factors prevents cardiac deaths in 90.5% of men and 82.1% of women. Similar findings have recently been reported in an analysis of lower risk populations, [9] underscoring that MetS is associated with CAD risk that is not entirely accounted for by traditional CAD risk scoring paradigms. These findings indicate that MetS treatment can greatly impact clinical outcomes.

MetS-associated increases in adiposity may be an important component of this syndrome. The NHANES III has shown increased visceral adipose tissue, i.e. central obesity measured by waist circumference, exacerbates the risk for MetS. [15] In that study of 14,924 men and women high waist circumference values were associated with virtually a two-fold increased prevalence of MetS irrespective if a person was normal weight, overweight, or obese. Yet, the risk of MetS increases as a function of body adiposity. [16] Increased body adiposity increases visceral adipose tissue and MetS risk [17] while exercise-induced weight loss reduces central obesity. [18] Hence, interventions aimed at body weight reduction can reduce the risk of MetS.

Reaven [19] is recognized for his seminal work showing that a number of metabolic disturbances reflecting increased coronary artery disease (CAD) risk are associated with insulin resistance. These metabolic disturbances are clinically manifested as overlapping conditions that include insulin resistance, MetS, and Type II diabetes mellitus. Current evidence suggests that a high accumulation of visceral adipose tissue (i.e., central obesity measured by waist circumference) is a main cause of insulin resistance that can be causally involved in the etiology of many MetS components. [20-22] Although the molecular basis of this condition is complicated and remains to be clarified, a current unifying hypothesis is that this condition arises from increased intracellular fatty acids that may interfere with pathways involved with glucose transport. [23] Recent findings indicate that impaired mitochondrial ATP production constitutes an underlying predisposition to this condition. [24] Ultimately insulin resistance develops in obesity and MetS because of alterations in partitioning of fat between adipocytes and the muscle and liver. Intracellular accumulation of fatty acid metabolites in insulin-responsive tissues (i.e., hepatic and skeletal muscle) rather than in adipocytes causes insulin signaling defects and insulin resistance. These alterations in glucose transport activity are likely the result of dysregulation of intramyocellular fatty acid metabolism, whereby fatty acids cause insulin resistance by activation of a serine kinase cascade, leading to decreased insulin-stimulated insulin receptor substrate (IRS)-1 tyrosine phosphoinositol 3-kinase (P13K) activity, a required step in insulin stimulated glucose transport into muscle via GLUT4, a glucose transporter. [23,25]

These findings support the current National Cholesterol Educational Program Adult Treatment Panel (NCEPATP) guidelines recommending long-term participation in total lifestyle change (TLC) weight loss programs of diet and physical exercise intervention for preventing and treating MetS. [6] Most components of MetS are related separately to lifestyle factors such as weight control, [26] diet, [27-31] and physical activity. [32-34] Although dietary interventions are a fundamental component of TLC programs aimed at weight reduction, physical activity and exercise play a pivotal in reinforcing and sustaining long-term weight loss. A recent call to action for clinicians emphasizes the importance of physical activity for reducing the global obesity epidemic. [1,5] The purpose of this article is to review and describe MetS including approaches for implementing physical activity in the context of TLC interventions. These include center- and phone-based programs as well as provider-based interventions.

BACKGROUND

In this section, we first review the rationale for the role of physical exercise training in reducing MetS. Then we review the current guidelines that recommend physical activity interventions aimed at weight reduction and the basis for these recommendations. Next we briefly discuss the current recommendations regarding TLC programs for reducing MetS. Finally we review the barriers to implementing physical exercise and TLC programs, describe programs that have been successfully implemented, and the elements of these programs that serve as the theoretical underpinnings of provider-based exercise interventions.

The Role of Physical Exercise Training in Reducing MetS

Physical exercise is a potent intervention for the prevention and treatment of MetS and its clinical sequelae. The term 'physical exercise training' is often misused as being synonymous with 'leisure time physical activity'. Physical exercise training can be defined as repeated bouts of exercise aimed at increasing physical performance (i.e., maximal aerobic capacity {VO_{2max}}) for the purpose of athleticism and competition rather than for health promotion and disease prevention, while leisure time physical activity includes all of the non-occupational physical pursuits that are encompassed in daily living, including physical exercise training. [35] While the term 'leisure time physical activity' is often semantically used in this context for the purposes of our discussion we will use the term physical activity in this connotation to indicate *moderate intensity physical activity* exemplified by walking.

Exercise-induced improved insulin sensitivity and reduction in the risk for diabetes mellitus and MetS result largely from modest (5 to 10 percent) reductions in adiposity. Recently Watkins et al. [36] evaluated the effects of a 6 month low fat, hypocaloric dietary program in conjunction with a walking-jogging program of approximately 35 minutes 3 to 4 times weekly on insulin sensitivity (a surrogate of MetS). Among the 53 men and women randomized to receive i.) Exercise only (n = 21), ii.) Exercise plus diet (n = 21), or iii.) Control (n = 11) those with exercise plus diet showed the greatest amount of reduction in body adiposity and largest amount of improvements in insulin response. In a randomized trial of patients with type 2 diabetes mellitus, patients who performed high intensity aerobic physical exercise training 3 times per week for 2 months increased aerobic capacity by 41% and insulin sensitivity by 46%. [37] Physical exercise causes increased insulin sensitivity in those who exercise on a regular basis. [38,39] Exercise training does not correct but compensates for the defects in muscle insulin resistance by increasing the expression of GLUT4 (cellular glucose receptors). [40] Heightened insulin sensitivity appears to be mediated by post-receptor insulin signaling, specifically at the distal steps of the insulin/P13K-signaling cascade, that leads to GLUT4 translocation and increased cellular uptake of serum glucose. [41-43] Physical exercise training-induced weight loss preferentially reduces visceral adipose tissue. [18,44] Randomized, controlled trials have shown that physical exercise training reduces intra-abdominal adiposity by approximately 28% in obese men [45] and over 20% in older and 17% in younger normal weight men [46] in a dose-response manner. [47] Physical exercise training has been shown to reduce prevalence of MetS. The HERITAGE Study showed that 105 subjects with MetS reduced the prevalence of MetS by 30.5% following a 20-week aerobic physical exercise training program. [48]

Current Guidelines Recommend Participation in Moderate Intensity Physical Activity (PA) not PET

Although physical exercise training can effectively reduce MetS risk, pragmatically it has not been shown to be effective because people are unwilling to participate in long-term physical exercise training. This problem has been recognized in the current guidelines of the Centers for Disease Control and the American College of Sports Medicine [49] and Healthy People 2010 [50] who recommend participation in moderate intensity physical activity 150 minutes /week (i.e., 30 minutes 5 days per week). Walking exemplifies a common form of moderate intensity physical activity. Leaf et al. [51] evaluated the feasibility of a calorie expenditure program for prescribing physical activity among community-dwelling elderly individuals using a 20 week center-based walking intervention. Center-based interventions provided at entry, 2, 6, and 10 weeks gradually advanced weekly calorie expenditure in a home-based walking program from 300 calories at entry to 1,200 calories at week 10. Walking was prescribed in terms of minutes needed to be walked each day to achieve the weekly calorie expenditure goal that was individualized based upon each person's customary walking speed and body weight. Nineteen of the initial 20 men and women (mean age $\pm$ SD = 71.2 $\pm$ 5 years) who entered the study were successfully participating in the program at the 20-week conclusion.

Moderate intensity physical activity is also associated with reduced total- and CAD-related mortality. [52,53] Ongoing participation in regular physical activity is critical for reducing CAD: Paffenbarger et al. [54] have shown that current participation in regular physical activity rather than a remote personal history of athleticism confers CAD risk reduction. The effect of physical activity on CAD risk reduction is likely multi-factorial and may not specifically affect atherogenesis: Physical activity reduces oxidative stress, [55] and thrombogenesis. [56] Yet, a major mechanism by which physical activity lowers CAD risk involves exercise-mediated reductions in the components that comprise the constellation of MetS-defining criteria: Body adiposity, [57,58] insulin resistance, [59] blood pressure, [60] and plasma lipids and lipoproteins (physical activity lowers triglycerides and raises plasma HDL-cholesterol levels). [58,61-63] Physical activity is an important modality for promoting long-term weight loss. [64,65] Women randomized to participate in regular physical activity, especially walking, a frequently used form of physical activity, had significant reductions in total body fat and intra-abdominal fat during a 12-month period compared with non-exercising women. [66,67] Long-term weight loss is more effectively sustained by higher volumes of regular physical activity as compared to modest amounts. [68]

Sedentary behavior has recently been associated with increased MetS risk. [4] Epidemiological studies indicate that physical activity exerts a protective effect from insulin resistance and type 2 diabetes mellitus. [69-71] A recent Finnish cohort study of 2,017 men and 2,352 women followed for a 9.4 year period found that sedentary behavior was associated with increased risk for new-onset diabetes mellitus with i.) both obesity and insulin resistance, ii.) either obesity or insulin resistance, and iii.) a normal BMI without insulin resistance. [70] Similarly a study of 1,069 men without diabetes mellitus or CAD who participated in the Kuopio Ischemic Heart Disease Risk Factor Study found those who engaged in at least moderate intensity physical activity for < 1 hour per week were 60 percent more likely to have MetS than those engaging in > 3 hours per week even after adjusting for confounders. [71] These findings underscore the importance of moderate intensity physical activity for reducing the progression of insulin-resistance and its associated CAD-related sequelae.

Program-Based Interventions for Reducing MetS

The key to addressing MetS is a lifestyle intervention program. TLC intervention programs combining dietary counseling with moderate intensity physical activity have been successful for weight reduction. [72,73] Typically this involves weight loss resulting from a combination of dietary counseling and increased physical activity and has been shown to reduce the prevalence of insulin resistance/diabetes mellitus [72] and its MetS-related components. [43]

Maintaining changes in both dietary and exercise behaviors are important for improving long-term weight loss. [69,70] Men and women randomized to receive either conventional aerobic-based PET or a physical activity program had a similar magnitude in reductions of body fat after two years. [60] A recent study by Jakicic et al. [73] supports the current guideline recommendations [49,50] regarding the degree of exercise intensity required to promote and sustain weight loss. Among 201 sedentary women randomized to receive i.) vigorous intensity/high duration, ii.) moderate intensity/high duration, iii.) moderate intensity/moderate duration, or iv.) vigorous intensity/moderate duration accompanied by a low fat, hypocaloric diet showed no significant differences in the amount of weight reduction after 12 months (i.] 8.9 ± 7.3 kg, ii.] 8.2 ± 7.6 kg, iii.] 6.3 ± 5.6 kg, and iv.] 7.0 ± 6.4 kg). Moreover a TLC program of moderate intensity PA in conjunction with a hypocaloric, low-fat diet can reduce insulin resistance and the risk for diabetes mellitus as has been demonstrated by the prototype model implemented by The Diabetes Prevention Program Research Group [72] that is described later.

Barriers to PA and Programs Aimed at Reducing these Barriers

Although participation in a 20-week exercise program is adequate to substantially reduce the prevalence of MetS and MetS-associated risk factors in a primary prevention setting, [48] long-term participation in PA is essential to sustain body weight and MetS-risk reduction. Despite the recommended Centers for Disease Control/American College of Sports Medicine and Exercise [49] and Healthy People 2010 [50] guidelines for increasing physical activity to control body weight, the majority of adults remain inactive. [5] Patients like many other individuals, are unlikely to participate in long-term exercise programs due to such factors as inconvenience and the expense of frequent travel to their exercise sessions. [74]

The Health Belief Model [75] posits that people are more likely to action if they believe that they are vulnerable or susceptible to the consequences of a behavior. Furthermore, people need to believe they are capable of changing their lifestyles and that these changes will lead to positive outcomes. Table 2. Summarizes the four basic conditions for behavioral change.

Table 2. Four Basic Conditions for Behavioral Change

a)	Awareness and understanding of information
b)	Awareness of potential benefit of change
c)	Individual feels able to perform activity or habit
d)	Accessible mode of change and supportive social environment.

The major barriers to physical exercise include:

i) Willingness to exercise,
ii) Ability to exercise, and
iii) Adherence to exercise.

i) Willingness to Exercise

Change in physical activity participation can be conceptualized in health-behavior theoretical models as a dynamic process with individuals moving through a series of stages as they adopt and maintain a new behavior, recognizing that recidivism is part of this process. [76,78,79] Although this model was initially developed to explain the stages and processes involved in smoking cessation [77], it has since been employed in exercise behavior. [78,81] Individuals can be categorized into stages of motivational readiness for exercise participation. [80,82-84] Young et al. [85] recently demonstrated that the stage of motivational readiness predicts adherence to a 9 month exercise intervention in 342 men and women randomized to receive; i.) diet intervention only, ii.) exercise intervention only, iii.) diet plus exercise interventions, or iv.) delayed intervention (i.e., control). The questionnaire identified exercise activities including brisk walking, jogging, swimming, and aerobic dancing and classifies individuals into 5 stages of readiness to exercise categories based on their responses to a series of statements. These stages include; a.) pre-contemplation, b.) contemplation, c.) preparation, d.) action, and e.) maintenance. The study used self-reported activity logs to define exercise adherence (i.e., the monthly volume summary score). Because of the small numbers of participants reported being in the pre-contemplation phase at baseline, this stage was not evaluated, and the action and maintenance stages were combined for the analysis. For men exercise intervention goals were reached by 54% who were in the contemplation stage, 69% in the preparation stage, and 68% in the action/maintenance stage. For women exercise intervention goals were reached by 35% who were in the contemplation stage, 67% in the preparation stage, and 24% in the action/maintenance stage. These findings indicate that the motivational readiness to exercise questionnaire can be used to identify individuals who are most likely to participate in long-term physical exercise.

ii) Ability to Exercise

Physical limitations such as spinal cord injury and limb amputation can limit the ability to exercise as can debilitating medical vascular conditions such as CAD, cerebrovascular accidents and peripheral arterial disease. For these conditions rehabilitative rather than 'wellness' programs are the preferred setting for exercise.

iii) Adherence to Exercise

Long-term adherence to exercise is historically low and approaches 60 percent after one year. [86,87] Adherence issues can be grossly dichotomized as a) program logistics, and b) sustained behavioral motivation.

a) Program Logistics

The low adherence to participation in long-term on-site exercise programs has been an impetus to explore other program logistics that may increase exercise accessibility including home- and community-based venues. *Home-based* exercise programs have been evaluated by King et al. [87] in a trial randomizing 160 women and 197 men to either 52-week programs of; i.) higher-intensity group-based exercise training, ii.) higher-intensity home-based exercise training, and iii.) lower-intensity home-based exercise training. Participants in the group-based programs attended 3 sessions each week for once year while the participants in the home-based programs received phone contact once per week for the first 4 weeks, biweekly for the following 4 weeks, then one monthly for 12 months. This study found one-year adherence greater in higher intensity (80%) and lower-intensity (76%) home-based programs than in the higher-intensity group-based program (44%). Moreover when those in each group who had completed at least 75% of the prescribed exercise sessions were compared the higher-intensity home–based program increased VO_{2max} to a greater extent than did its group-based counterpart. *Community-based* exercise interventions have been evaluated in the Community Healthy Activities Model Program for Seniors (CHAMPS) showing that referral to a community-based program that provides exercise resources as part of a comprehensive plan to increase physical activity levels among seniors contributed to a greater percentage of subjects in the intervention group (68%) compared with a non-intervention group (35%) who were physically active after 6 months. [88] More recently CHAMPS II, based on the earlier CHAMPS, evaluated the effect of a lifestyle program that promoted increased physical activity levels for older adults based upon a personal choice model. [89] Subjects recruited from a large multi-specialty group practice were randomized to receive a 1-year physical activity promotion program or to a wait-list control group. The program provided individualized client-centered motivational, behavioral, and cognitive techniques to encourage participants to join classes and programs in the community and/or develop an exercise program of their own. The results of this program showed those randomized to receive the exercise intervention significantly increased their physical activity levels compared with the control group. These findings indicate that programs utilizing self-directed community-based physical exercise resources can greatly improve long-term exercise success.

b) Sustained Behavioral Motivation

Behavioral theories such as social cognitive theory [90] underscore the importance of ongoing monitoring, follow-up, and feedback in helping to facilitate sustained adherence to physical activity and other health promotion interventions. [90] The 'case management' approach [91,92] relying heavily on telephone contacts has been found to be consistently effective in community-based exercise promotion trials. [87,88,93,94] A recent study with elderly VA primary care patients demonstrated increased home-based walking and fitness over one year using case management nurse counseling with telephone and mail follow-up. [95]

SUCCESSFUL TLC PROGRAMS

The most successful programs for TLC that will be discussed later, such as the Diabetes Prevention Program, [72] involve both weight loss and physical activity initiating with more intensive weekly center-based sessions that then fade to lower intensity as the program progresses. [72,73] However, the application of these programs may be limited because patients may have difficulty in attending program sessions. Phone-based programs, although less likely to be as effective in causing weight loss, may be more effectively implemented because of their convenience and provide fewer barriers to access to a larger group of patients.

Although home- and community-based programs have *both* generally been regarded to achieve good physical activity adherence they have minimal impact in affecting and sustaining clinically significant weight loss necessary to reduce MetS risk. Successful programs for TLC involving both weight loss through diet and physical activity have used center-based reinforcement sessions with dietary counseling initially administered on a weekly basis which then fade to lower intensity as the program progresses. [72,93,94] The Trial of Nonpharmacologic Interventions in the elderly (TONE) a randomized study in men and women aged 60 to 80 years aimed at achieving and maintaining a 4.5 kg. weight loss combined with dietary sodium restriction exemplifies this approach. [57] Subjects receiving the lifestyle intervention met with nutrition and exercise counselors in individual and small group sessions on a regular basis and had a 4.7 kg weight reduction after 30 weeks compared with the 0.9 kg weight reduction in those receiving usual care.

Recently the Diabetes Prevention Program Research Group employed a 16-lesson center-based TLC program that administered a curriculum covering diet, exercise, and behavior in conjunction with a dietary and physical activity programs to help participants achieve and maintain their goal of a 7 percent weight loss [72] in a group of 3,234 non-diabetics who were at high-risk for diabetes mellitus. The two major goals of the Diabetes Prevention Program lifestyle intervention were; i.) a minimum of 7% weight loss/weight maintenance and ii.) a minimum of 150 min/week of physical activity similar in intensity to brisk walking. Both goals were hypothesized to be feasible, safe, and effective based on previous clinical trials in other countries. [89-93] The methods used to achieve these lifestyle goals include the following key features: 1) individual case managers or "lifestyle coaches;" 2) frequent contact with participants; 3) a structured, state-of-the-art, 16-session core-curriculum that taught behavioral self-management strategies for weight loss and physical activity; 4) supervised physical activity sessions; 5) a more flexible maintenance intervention, combining group and individual approaches, motivational campaigns, and "restarts;" 6) individualization through a "toolbox" of adherence strategies; 7) tailoring of materials and strategies to address ethnic diversity; and finally 8) an extensive network of training, feedback, and clinical support. [96-100] The curriculum, taught by case managers in a face-to-face center-based venue was administered on a weekly basis for the first 8 weeks, biweekly for the next 16 weeks, then monthly for the remainder of the long-term intervention. Those receiving this center-based LTC intervention were more successful in sustaining weight loss and reduced their incidence of diabetes by 58% after a 3-year follow-up period compared with the non-intervention group.

Phone-based interventions have been used successfully in medical case-management [91] and for promoting physical activity. [87,88,95] This intervention modality is attractive because it represents a potentially inexpensive and convenient form of intervention. In many areas of health promotion, minimal treatment interventions are being evaluated to address the issue of treatment practicality. Minimal intensity treatment approaches such as correspondence programs are often rated as more preferable than face-to-face formats [103] but there are mixed results when applying minimal interventions weight loss. [104-108] One type of minimal intervention, phone calls and mailings, have been used successfully as a maintenance strategy for weight loss [109] and to assist in managing weight over the holiday season. [110] However, phone calls and mailings were less effective in other studies. [111] Recently Boutelle et al. [112] employed an 8–week minimal intervention dietary-based weight loss program that involved weekly educational mailings and phone calls (5 minutes) in a group of 26 obese (BMI = 34.7 $\pm$ 4.9) Veteran men. Those randomized to receive this intervention showed a tendency for increased weight reduction (3.9 $\pm$ 6.1 lbs) compared with the control patients (1.6 $\pm$ 3.3 lbs) after 8 weeks. The findings from this study suggest that a similar program of longer duration and involving more intensive telephone intervention sessions in a larger group of patients. Phone-based programs are regarded to be as effective as center-based programs for increasing participation in physical activity. However, as discussed, center-based TLC interventions have a more substantial impact on weight reduction than currently studied phone-based interventions. Phone-based interventions providing TLC interventions that are more intensive both in content and duration than those previously described are potentially an alternative for patients who cannot or will not attend center-based TLC sessions. Hence, phone-based interventions, although less effective on an individual basis, potentially can involve a larger population of patients than home-based interventions. Such a phone-based TLC intervention merits comparison with conventionally established face-to-face center-based interventions such as the one administered by the Diabetes Prevention Program.

PRACTITIONER-BASED INTERVENTIONS FOR REDUCING METS

Although exercise guidelines indicate that practitioners should have an active role in promoting physical activity, health practitioners do not routinely counsel patients about physical activity in the usual care-wellness setting [113] and focus primarily on patients who are at high risk for disease. [114] The Activity Counseling Trial (ACT) was a multi-center trial that randomized 395 women and 479 men to receive i.) physician advice with educational materials, ii.) physician advice plus interactive mail and behavioral counseling assistance at physician visits, or iii.) physician advice and assistance plus regular investigator-initiated phone counseling and behavioral classes. [115] After 24 months among women VO_{2max} was greater in the assistance (group ii.) and the counseling (group iii.) groups than in the advice group (group i.) although no group differences in levels of self-reported physical activity were noted. No differences were noted among the groups of men for either VO_{2max} or self-reported physical activity. These findings indicate that exercise promotion when provided in the usual primary care setting may not be adequate to substantially affect long-term physical activity behaviors. However, although program-based TLC interventions can play an important role in reducing MetS, the role of the clinician to successfully impact TLC success has been emphasized. [5]

The 33rd Bethesda Conference on Preventive Cardiology identified a need to understand better the barriers to professional adherence to prevention guidelines a the community, provider, and patient levels. [116] The conference urges placing special focus groups on vulnerable groups, including the economically disadvantaged, elderly individuals, and ethnic minorities. A recent survey of medical residents and attending physicians in a large, urban public hospital identified 2 main barriers to effective prevention counseling: lack of training in prevention, and our system's emphasis on acute care rather than preventive care. [117]

In order to be successful the clinician must believe that the patient is capable of change, and must understand the ABCs, i.e. attitude, beliefs, and core values of the patient. Prior to TLC counseling it is important for a clinician to obtain information regarding the patient's lifestyle in order to tailor TLC counseling to the individual. Moreover a medical history and physical examination can identify patients with medical conditions that require rehabilitative exercise interventions. Suggesting one change at a time, i.e. single concept learning is more effective than trying to persuade patients to change their entire behavior pattern. According to Bandura's Social Learning Theory, behavior is learned and can be unlearned. [90] People learn most effectively when they are actively involved in the decision-making process and believe that they can change. The provider and patient should collaborate in developing a plan and setting goals for behavior change. Although individuals need adequate information on which to base a decision to change they must also believe in their own ability to make changes and must be encouraged to strive for positive outcomes. Individuals need the skills, support, and resources tailored to them. The goal for physical activity should be specific. Although current recommendations suggest 30 minutes of moderate intensity a day on at least 5 days a week, this recommendation may not seem meaningful to most patients. In this context a specific goal would be to 'take an evening stroll with the family'.

CONCLUSIONS

While TLC interventions to reduce MetS are a public health imperative, the most effective interventions remain to be defined. Successful center-, phone-, and provider-based interventions need to adhere to similar theoretical underpinnings. Current findings suggest that there may be an overlap in the effectiveness in the use of these various approaches, and, as is apparent for lifestyle change programs, these different forms of intervention may be complementary to each other. Indeed further studies are important to delineate how these different approaches can best be employed to reduce the risk for MetS.

REFERENCES

[1]   Mokdad AH, Bowman BA, Ford ES, Vinicor F, Marks JS, Koplan JP. The continuing epidemics of obesity and diabetes in the United States. *JAMA*. 2001; 286:1195-2000.
[2]   Flegal KM, Carroll MD, Ogden CL, Johnson CL. Prevalence and trends in obesity among US adults. *JAMA*. 2003; 289:76-79.
[3]   Ford ES, Giles WH, Dietz WH. Prevalence of the metabolic syndrome among US adults. Findings from the Third National Health and Nutrition Examination Survey. *JAMA*. 2002; 287:356-359.
[4]   Park Y-W, Zhu S, Palaniappan L, Heshka S, Carnethon MR, Heymsfield SB. The metabolic syndrome. Prevalence and associated risk factor findings in the US population from the Third National Health and Nutrition Examination Survey, 1988-1994. *Arch Intern Med*. 2003; 163:427-436.
[5]   Manson JE, Skerret PJ, Greenland, Van Itallie TB. The escalating pandemics of obesity and sedentary lifestyle. A call to action for clinicians. *Arch Intern Med*. 2004; 164:249-258.
[6]   Expert Panel on Detection, Evaluation, and Treatment of High blood Cholesterol In Adults. Executive summary of the third report of the

National Cholesterol Education Program Expert Panel on Detection, Evaluation, and Treatment of High Blood Cholesterol in Adults. *JAMA.* 2001; 285:2486-2497.

[7]   Laaksonen DE, Lakka HM, Niskanen LK, Kaplan GA, Salonen JT, Lakka TA. Metabolic syndrome and development of diabetes mellitus: application and validation of recently suggested definition of the metabolic syndrome. *Am J Epidemiol.* 2002; 156:1070-1077.

[8]   Sattar N, Gaw A, Scherbakova O, et al. Metabolic syndrome with and without C- reactive protein as a predictor of coronary heart disease and diabetes in the West of Scotland Coronary Prevention Study. *Circulation.* 2003; 108:414-419.

[9]   Girman CJ, Rhodes T, Mercuri M, et al. The metabolic syndrome and risk of major events in the Scandanavian Simvastatin Survival Study (4S) and the Air Force/Texas Coronary Atherosclerosis Prevention Study (AFCAPS/TexCAPS). *Am J Cardiol.* 2004; 93:136-141.

[10]   HuG, Quiao Q, Tuomilehto J, Balkau B, Borch-Johnsen K, and Pyorala K. Prevalence of the metabolic syndrome and its relation to all-cause and cardiovascular mortality in nondiabetic European men and women. *Arch Intern Med.* 2004; 164:1066-1076.

[11]   Solymoss BC, Bourassa MG, Campeua L, Sniderman A, Marcil M, Lesperance J, Levesque S, and Varga S. Effect of increasing metabolic syndrome score on atherosclerotic risk profile and coronary artery disease angiographic severity. *Am J Cardiol.* 2004; 93:159-164.

[12]   Pyorala M, Miettinen H, Halonen P, Laakso M, Pyorala K. Insulin resistance syndrome predicts the risk of coronary heart disease and stroke in healthy middle-aged men: the 22-year follow-up results of the Helsinki Policemen Study. *Circulation.* 1998; 98:398-404.

[13]   Arad Y, Newstein D, Cadet F, Roth M, Guerci AD. Association of multiple risk factors and insulin resistance with increased prevalence of asymptomatic coronary artery disease by electron-beam computed tomographic study. *Arterioscler Thromb Vasc Biol.* 2001; 21:2051-2058.

[14]   Wong ND, Pio JR, Franklin SS, L'Italien GJ, Kamath TV, Williams GR. Preventing coronary events by optimal control of blood pressure and lipids in patients with the metabolic syndrome. *Am J Cardiol.* 2003; 91:1421-1426.

[15]   Janssen I, Katzmarzyk PT, Ross R. Body mass index, waist circumference, and health risk. Evidence in support of current National Institute of Health guidelines. *Arch Intern Med.* 2002; 162:2074-2079.

[16] Ashton WD, Nanchahal K, Wood DA. Body mass index and metabolic risk factors for coronary heart disease in women. *Eur Heart J.* 2001; 22:46-55.

[17] Haffner SM, Mykkanen L, Festa A, Burke J, Stern M. Insulin resistant pre-diabetic subjects have more atherogenic risk factors than insulin sensitive pre-diabetic subjects: implications for preventing coronary heart disease during the pre-diabetic state. *Circulation.* 2000; 101:975-980.

[18] Slenz CA, Duscha BD, Johnson JL, et al. Effects of the amount of exercise on body weight, body composition, and measures of central obesity. STRRIDE- a randomized controlled study. *Arch Intern Med.* 2004; 164:31-39.

[19] Reaven GN. Role of insulin resistance in human disease. *Diabetes.* 1988; 37:1596-1607.

[20] Lemieus S, Despres JP. Metabolic complications of visceral obesity: contribution to the aetiology of type 2 diabetes and implications for prevention and treatment. *Diabetes Metab.* 1994; 20:375-393.

[21] Despres JP. Visceral obesity: A component of the insulin resistance dyslipidemic syndrome. *Can J Cardiol.* 1994; 10:17B-22B.

[22] Haffner SM. The insulin resistance syndrome revisited. *Diabetes Care.* 1996; 19:275-277.

[23] Shulman GI. Cellular mechanisms of insulin resistance. *J Clin Invest.* 2000; 206:171-176.

[24] Petersen KF, Dufour S, Befroy D, Garcia R, Shulman GI. Impaired mitochondrial activity in the insulin-resistant offspring of patients with type 2 diabetes. *N Engl J Med.* 2004; 350:664-671.

[25] Shuldine AR, McLenithan. Genes and the pathophysiology of type 2 diabetes: more than just the Randle cycle all over again. *J Clin Invest.* 2004; 114:1414-1417.

[26] Reaven GM. Diet and syndrome X. *Curr Atherosler Rep.* 2000; 2:503-507.

[27] Abbassi F, McLaughlin T, Lamendola C, et al. High carbohydrate diets, triglyceride-rich lipoproteins, and coronary heart risk. *Am J Cardiol.* 2000; 85:45-48.

[28] Wirtalt E, Hedblad B, Guilberg B, et al. Food patterns and components of the metabolic syndrome in men and women: a cross-sectional study within the Malmo Diet and Cancer cohort. *Am J Epidemiol.* 2001; 154:1150-1159.

[29] Ludwig DS, Periera MA, Kroenke CH, et al. Dietary fiber, weight gain, and cardiovascular disease risk factors in young adults. *JAMA.* 1999; 282:1539-1546.

[30] Periera MA, Jacobs DRJ, Van Horn L, Stattery ML, Kartashov AI, Ludwig DS. Dietary consumption, obesity, and the insulin resistance syndrome in young adults in the CARDIA Study. *JAMA*. 2002; 287:2081-2089.

[31] Fung TT, Rimm EB, Spiegelman D, et al. Association between dietary patterns and plasma biomarkers of obesity and cardiovascular disease risk. *Am J Clin Nutr*. 2001; 73:61-67.

[32] Miyatake N, Nishikawa H, Morishita A, et al. Daily walking reduces visceral adipose tissue areas and improves insulin resistance in Japanese obese subjects. *Diabetes Res Clin Pract*. 2002; 58:101-107.

[33] Meigs JB, D'Agostino RBSr, Wilson PWF, Cupples LA, Nathan DM, Singer DE. Risk variable clustering in the insulin resistance syndrome. The Framingham Offspring Study. *Diabetes*. 1997; 46:1494-1600.

[34] McAuley KA, Williams SM, Mann JI, et al. Intensive lifestyle changes are necessary to improve insulin sensitivity: a randomized controlled trial. *Diabetes Care*. 2002; 25:445-452.

[35] Caspersen CJ, CJ, Powell KE, Christensen GM. Physical activity, exercise, and physical fitness. *Public Health Rep*. 1985; 100:125-131.

[36] Watkins LL, Sherwood A, Feinglos M, Hinderliter A, Babyak M, Gullette E, Waugh R, Blumenthal JA. Effects of exercise and weight loss on cardiac risk factors associated with Syndrome X. *Arch Intern Med*. 2003; 163:1889-1895.

[37] Mourier A, Gautier JF, De Kerviler E. Mobilization of visceral adipose tissue related to the improvement in insulin sensitivity in response to physical exercise training in NIDDM: effects of branched-chain amino acid supplements. *Diabetes Care*. 1997; 20:385-391.

[38] Kirwan JP, del Aguila LF, Hernandez JM, Williamson DL, O' Gorman DJ, Lewis R, Krishman RK. Regular exercise enhances insulin activation of IRS-associated PI3-kinase in human skeletal muscle. *J Appl Physiol*. 2000; 88:797-803.

[39] Kirwan JP, Jing M. Modulation of insulin signaling in human skeletal muscle in response to exercise. *Exerc Sport Sci Rev*. 2002; 30:85-90.

[40] Ivy JL. Muscle insulin resistance amended with exercise training: Role of GLUT4 Expression. *Med Sci Sports Exerc*. 2004; 36:1207-1211.

[41] Hawley JA, Houmard JA. Preventing insulin resistance through exercise: a cellular approach. *Med Sci Sports Exerc*. 2004; 36:1187-1190.

[42] Berggren JR, Hulver MW, Dohm GL, Houmard JA. Weight loss and exercise: implications for muscle lipid metabolism and insulin action. *Med Sci Sports Exerc*. 2004; 136:1191-1195.

[43] Bruce CR, Hawley JA. Improvements in insulin resistance with aerobic exercise training: A lipocentric approach. *Med Sci Sports Exerc.* 2004; 136:1196-1201.

[44] Mayo MJ, Grantham JR, Balasekaran G. Exercise-induced weight loss preferentially reduces abdominal fat. *Med Sci Sports Exerc.* 2003; 35:207-213.

[45] Ross R, Dagone D, Jones PJH, Smith H, Paddags A, Hudson R, Janssen. Reduction in obesity and related comorbid conditions after diet-induced weight loss or exercise-induced weight loss in men. *Ann Intern Med.* 2000; 133:92-103.

[46] Schwartz RS, Shuman WP, Larson V, Cain KC, Fellingham GW, Beard JC, Kahn SE, Stratton JR, Cerqueira MD, Abass IB. The effect of intensive endurance exercise training on body fat distribution in young and older men. *Metabolism.* 1991; 40:545-551.

[47] Ross R, Janssen I. Physical activity, total and regional obesity: dose response considerations. *Med Sci Sports Exerc.* 2001; 33:S521-527.

[48] Katzmarzyk PT, Leon AS, Wilmore JH, skinner JS, Rao DC, Rankinen T, Bouchard C. Targeting the metabolic syndrome with exercise: Evidence from the HERITAGE Family Study. *Med Sci Sports Exerc.* 2003; 35:1703-1709.

[49] Pate RR, Pratt M, Blair SN. Physical Activity and Public Health. A recommendation from the Centers for Disease Control and Prevention and the American College of Sports Medicine. *JAMA.* 995; 273:402-407.

[50] Healthy People 2010: Volume II. Conference Edition. Washington DC: USD Dept of Health and Human Services: 2000.

[51] Leaf DA, Reuben DB. "Lifestyle" interventions for promoting physical activity: A kilocalorie expenditure-based home feasibility study. *Am J Med Sci.* 1996; 312:68-75.

[52] Lee I-M, Skerrett PJ. Physical activity and all-cause mortality: what is the dose-response relation? *Med Sci Sports Exerc.* 2001; 33:S459-S471.

[53] Leon AS, Connett J, Jacobs DR, Rauramaa R. Leisure –time physical activity nd risk of coronary heart disease and death: the Multiple Risk Factor Intervention Trial. *JAMA.* 1987; 258:2386-2396.

[54] Paffenbarger RS, Hyde RT, Wing AL, Hsieh C.-C. Physical activity, all-cause mortality and longevity of college alumni. *N Engl J Med.* 1986; 314:605-614.

[55] Leaf DA, Kleinman MT, Hamilton M, Deitrick RW. The exercise-induced oxidative stress paradox: the effects of physical exercise training. *Am J Med Sci.* 1999; 317:295-300.

[56] Wannamethee SG, Lowe GDO, Whincup PH, Rumley A, Walker M, Lennon L. Physical activity and hemostatic and inflammatory variables in men. *Circulation.* 2002; 105:1785-1790.

[57] Whelton PK, Appel LJ, Espeland MA, et al. Sodium reduction and weight loss in the treatment of hypertension in older persons. A randomized controlled trial of Nonpharmacologic Interventions in the Elderly (TONE). *JAMA.* 1998; 279:839-846.

[58] Leaf DA, Parker DL, McAfee JR. The relationship of physical activity to CAD risk factors: Lipids, lipoproteins, percent body fat, and blood pressure. *J Cardiopulm Rehab.* 1989; 9(12): 497-505.

[59] Rankinen T, Suomela-Markkanene T, Vaisanene S, Helminen A, Penttila I, Berg A, Bouchard C, Rauramaa R. Relationship between changes in physical activity and plasma insulin during a 2.5-year follow-up study. *Metabolism.* 1997; 46:1418-1423.

[60] Dunn AL, Marcus BH, Kampert JB, Garcia ME, Kohl HL, Blair SN. Comparison of lifestyle and structured interventions to increase physical activity and cardiorespiratory fitness: a randomized trial. *JAMA.* 1999; 281:327-334.

[61] Bouchard C, Rankinen T. Individual differences in response to regular physical activity. *Med Sci Sports Exerc.* 2001; 33:S446-S451.

[62] Leaf DA, Parker DL, Schaad D. Changes in VO$_{2max}$, physical activity, and body fat with chronic exercise: effects of plasma lipids. *Med Sci Sports and Exerc.* 1997; 29:1152-1159.

[63] Duncan JJ, Gordon NF, Scott CB. Women walking for health and fitness. How much is enough? *JAMA.* 1991; 266:3291-3297.

[64] Jakicic JM, Gallagher KI. Exercise considerations for the sedentary, overweight adult. *Exerc Sport Sci Rev.* 2003; 31:91-95.

[65] Klem ML, Wing RR, McGuire MT, Seagle HM, Hill JO. A descriptive study of individuals successful at long-term maintenance of substantial weight loss. *Am J Clin Nutr.* 1997; 66:239-246.

[66] Jakicic JM, Winters C, Lang W, Wing RR. Effects of intermittent exercise and use of home exercise equipment on adherence, weight loss, and fitness in overweight women: a randomized trial. *JAMA.* 1999; 282:1554-1560.

[67] Irwin ML, Yasui Y, Ulrich CM, Bowen D, Rudolph RE, Schwartz RS, Yukawa M, Aiello E, Potter JD, McTiernan A. Effect of exercise on total and intra-abdominal body fat in post menopausal women, a randomized controlled trial. *JAMA.* 2003; 289:323-330.

[68] Jakicic JM, Wing RR, Butler BA, Robertson RJ. Prescribing exercise in multiple short bouts versus one continuous bout: effects of adherence,

cardiorespiratory fitness, and weight loss in overweight women. *Int J Obes.* 1995; 19:893-901.

[69]   Kelly DE, Goodpaster BH. The effects of exercise on glucose homeostasis in Type 2 diabetes mellitus. *Med Sci Sports Exerc.* 2001; 33:S495-S501.

[70]   Hu G, Lindstrom J, Valle T, Eriksson JG, Jousilahti P, Silventoinen K, Qiao Q, Tuomilehto J. Physical activity, body mass index, and risk of Type 2 diabetes in patients with normal or impaired glucose regulation. *Arch Intern Med.* 2004; 164:892-896.

[71]   Lakka TA, Laaksonen DE, Lakka H-M, Mannikko N, Niskanen LK, Rauramaa R, and Salonen JT. Sedentary lifestyle, poor cardiorespiratory fitness, and the metabolic syndrome. *Med Sci Sports Exerc.* 2003; 35:1279-1286.

[72]   Diabetes Prevention Program Research Group. Reduction in the incidence of type 2 diabetes with lifestyle intervention or metformin. *N Eng J Med.* 2002; 346:393-403.

[73]   Jakicic JM, Marcus BH, Gallagher KI, Napolitano M, Lang W. Effect of exercise duration and intensity on weight loss in overweight, sedentary women. *JAMA.* 2003; 290:1323-1330.

[74]   Marcus BH, Dubbert PM, Forsyth LH, McKenzie TL, Stone EJ, Dunn AL, Blair SN. Physical activity behavior change: Issues in adoption and maintenance. *Health Psychology.* 2000; 19(1,S): 32-41.

[75]   Rosenstock I. In Glanz K, et al., Eds. *Health Behavior and Education: Theory, Research and Practice.* San Francisco: Jossey-Bass, 1990.

[76]   Prochaska JO, Velicer WF. The transtheoretical model of health behavior change. *Am J Health Promotion.* 1997; 12:38-48.

[77]   Prochaska JO, DiClemente CC. Stages and processes of self-change of smoking: toward an integrative model of change. *J Consult Clin Psychol.* 1983,51:390-395.

[78]   Dishman RK. Compliance/adherence in health-related exercise. *Health Psychol.* 1982; 1:237-267.

[79]   Sallis JF, Haskell WL, Fortman S, et al. Predictors of adoption and maintenance of physical activity in a community sample. *Prev Med.* 1985; 15:331-341.

[80]   Marcus BH, Owen N. motivational readiness, self-efficacy and decision-making for exercise. *J Appl Social Psychol.* 1992; 22:3-16.

[81]   Marcus BH, Selby VS, Niaura RS, et al. Self-efficacy and the stages of exercise behavior change. *Res Q Exerc Sport.* 1992; 63:60-66.

[82]   Marcus BH, Rossi JS, Selby VC, et al. The stages and processes of exercise adoption and maintenance in a worksite sample. *Health Psychol.* 1992; 11:386-395.

[83]   Herrick AB, Stone WJ, Mettler MM. Stages of change, decisional balance, and self-efficacy across four health behaviors in a worksite environment. *Am J Health Promot.* 1997; 12:49-56.

[84]   Marcus BH, Pinto BM, Simkin LR, et al. Application of theoretical models to exercise behavior among employed women. *Am J Health Promot.* 1994; 49:49-55.

[85]   Young DR, King AC, Sheehan M, Stefaneik ML. Stage of motivational readiness: predictive ability for exercise behavior. *Am J Health Behav.* 2002; 26:331-341.

[86]   Dishman RK, Sallis JF, Orenstein DR. The determinants of physical activity and exercise. *Pub Health Rep.* 1985; 100; 158-171.

[87]   King AC, Haskell WL, Taylor B, Kraemer HC, DeBusk RF. Group-vs Home-based exercise training in healthy older men and women. A community-based clinical trial. *JAMA.* 1991; 266:1535-1542.

[88]   Stewart AL, Mills KM, Sepsis PG, King AC, McLellan BY, Roltz K, Ritter P. Evaluation of CHAMPS, A physical activity promotion program for older adults. *Ann Behav Med.* 1997; 19:353-361.

[89]   Stewart AL, Verboncoeur CJ, McLellan BY, et al. Physical activity outcomes of CHAMPS II: A physical activity promotion program for older adults. *J Gerontol.* 2000; 56A:M465-M470.

[90]   Bandura A. *Social foundations of thought and action: a social cognitive theory.* Englewood Cliffs, NJ: Prentice-Hall, 1986.

[91]   DeBusk RF, et al. A case-management system for coronary risk factor modification after acute myocardial infarction. *Ann Intern Med.* 1994:120; 721-729.

[92]   Wasson J, et al. Telephone care as a substitute for routine clinic follow-up. *JAMA.* 1992; 267:1788-1793.

[93]   Appel LJ, Champagne CM, Harsha DW, Cooper LS, Obarzenek E, Elmer PJ, Stevens VJ, Vollmer WM, Lin PH, Svetkey LP, Stedman SW, Young DR. Writing group of the PREMIER collaborative research group. *JAMA.* 2003; 289:2083-2093.

[94]   Ard JD, Grambow SC, Liu D, Slentz CA, Kras WE, Svetkey PL. The effect of the PREMIER interventions on insulin sensitivity. *Diabetes Care.* 2004; 27:340-347.

[95]   Dubbert PM, Cooper KM, Kirchner KK, Meydrech EM, and Bilbrew D. Effects of nurse counseling on walking for exercise in elderly primary care

patients. *Journal of Gerontology: Medical Sciences.* 2002; 57A:M733–M740.

[96] Eriksson KF, Lindgarde F: Prevention of type 2 (non-insulin-dependent) diabetes mellitus by diet and physical exercise. *Diabetologia.* 1991:34:891–898.

[97] Page RCL, Harnden KE, Cook JTE, Turner RC: Can life-styles of subjects with impaired glucose tolerance be changed? A feasibility study. *Diabet Med.* 1992; 9:562–566.

[98] Bourn DM, Mann JI, McSkimming BJ, Waldron MA, Wishart JD: Impaired glucose tolerance and NIDDM. Does a lifestyle intervention program have an effect? *Diabetes Care.* 1994; 17:1311–1319.

[99] Pan X-R, Li G-W, Hu Y-H, Wang J-X, Yang W-Y, An Z-X, Hu Z-X, Lin J, Xiao J-Z, Cao H-B, Liu P-A, Jiang X-G, Jiang Y-Y, Wang J-P, Zheng H, Zhang H, Bennett PH, Howard BV: Effects of diet and exercise in preventing NIDDM in people with impaired glucose tolerance: the Da Qing IGT and Diabetes Study. *Diabetes Care.* 1997; 20:537–544.

[100] Tuomilehto JLJ, Eriksson JG, Valle TT, Hamalainin H, Ilanne-Parikka P, Keinanen-Kiukaanniemi S, Laakso M, Louheranta A, Rastas M, Salminen V, Uusitupa M: Prevention of type 2 diabetes mellitus by changes in lifestyle among subjects with impaired glucose tolerance. *N Engl J Med.* 2001; 344:1343–1392.

[101] The Diabetes Prevention Program Research Group. The Diabetes Prevention Program (DPP) Research group. *Diabetes Care.* 2002; 25:2165–2171.

[102] www.bsc.gwu.edu/dpp/manuals.htmlvdoc

[103] Sherwood NE, Morton N, Jeffery RW, et al. Consumer preferences in format and type of community-based weight control programs. *Am J Health Promot.* 1998; 13:12-18.

[104] Jeffery RW, Hellerstedt WE, Schmid TL. Correspondence programs for smoking cessation and weight control: a comparison of two strategies in the Minnesota Heart Health Program. *Health Psychol.* 1990; 9:585-598.

[105] Cameron R, MacDonald MA, Schlegel PR, et al. Toward the development of self-help health behavior change programs: weight loss by correspondence. *Can J Public Health.* 1990; 81:2175-279.

[106] Jeffery RW, Danaher BG, Killen J, et al. Self-administered programs for health behavior change: smoking cessation and weight reduction by mail. *Addict Behav.* 1982; 7:57-63.

[107] O'Loughlin J, Paradis G, Meshefedjian G, et al. Evaluation of an 8-week mailed healthy-weight intervention. *Prev Med.* 1998; 27:288-95.

[108] Saelens BE, Sallis JF, Wilfley DE, et al. Behavioral weight control for overweight adolescents initiated in primary care. *Obes Res.* 2002; 10:22-32.

[109] Perri MG, Nezu AM, Patti ET, et al. Effect of length of treatment on weight loss. *J Consult Clin Psychol.* 1989; 57:450-452.

[110] Boutelle KN, Kirshenbaum DS, Baker RC, et al. How can obese weigh controllers minimize weight gain during the high risk holiday season? By self-monitoring very consistently. *Health Psychol.* 1999; 18:364-368.

[111] Hellerstedt WL, Jeffery RW. The effects of a telephone-based intervention on weight loss. *Am J Health Promot.* 1997; 11:177-182.

[112] Boutelle K, Dubbert PM, Vander Weg. A pilot study evaluating a minimum contact telephone and mail weight management intervention for primary care patients. *Eating and Weight Disorders* (In Press).

[113] Wee McCarthy EP, David RB, Phillips RS. Physician counseling about exercise. *JAMA.* 1999; 282:1583-1588.

[114] Wells KB, et al. The practices of general and subspecialty internists in counseling about smoking and exercise. *Am J Pub Health.* 1986; 76:1009-1013.

[115] The Writing Group of the ACT Research Group. The effects of physical activity counseling in primary care. The ACTS: A randomized control trial. *JAMA.* 2001; 286:677-687.

[116] Aedes PA, Kottke TE, Miller NH, et al. Task Force #3 – Getting results: who where, how? *J Am Coll Cardiol.* 2002; 40:615-629.

[117] Tsui JI, Dodson K, Jacobson TA. Cardiovascular disease prevention counseling in residency: resident and attending physician attitudes and practices. *J Natl Med Assoc.* 2004; 96:1080-1091.

In: Exercise and Health Research   ISBN: 978-1-60021-985-6
Editor: M. D. Johansen, pp. 123-136   © 2008 Nova Science Publishers, Inc.

Chapter 5

CORONARY ARTERY DISEASE RISK AMONG NATIVE AMERICANS: THE ISSUE OF OBESITY

David Alexander Leaf[*],

Departments of Medicine
VA Greater Los Angeles Healthcare System, David Geffen School of
Medicine at U.C.L.A, Los Angeles, California, USA

Stella Izuchukwu

Department of Medicine, VA Greater Los Angeles Healthcare System
David Geffen School of Medicine at U.C.L.A, Los Angeles, California, USA

ABSTRACT

Eliminating racial and ethnic disparities in coronary artery disease
(CAD) risk is an important public health goal. Although Native Americans
have been historically been perceived to be at low risk for CAD, recent
findings indicate a high prevalence of CAD risk factors exist in this
population. Much of this risk is a result of the increasing incidence of
overweight/obesity that can potentially be ameliorated by lifestyle
interventions aimed at weight reduction. The purpose of this article is to
promote awareness that Native Americans are a high-risk CAD population

[*] Address correspondence to: David Alexander Leaf, M.D., M.P.H., Division of General Internal
Medicine, 111G, Greater Los Angeles V.A. Healthcare System, Wilshire & Sawtelle Blvds. Los
Angeles, California, 90073. Tel (310) 268-3254; FAX (310) 268-4933; David.Leaf@med.va.gov.

and suggest strategies for lifestyle interventions aimed at obesity-related CAD risk reduction. These strategies emphasize overcoming barriers to behavioral change pertaining to dietary choices and promoting physical activity such as lack of healthy food supplies and transportation that are limited for many Native Americans. In addition, participation in total lifestyle change programs as well as individual practitioner counseling may have effective roles in reducing CAD risk among Native Americans.

Keywords: Native Americans, Obesity, Coronary Artery Disease

INTRODUCTION

Native Americans constitute geographically and culturally diverse populations that include American Indians who inhabit the continental United States and Canada, Alaskan Natives, Native Hawaiians, and Pacific Islanders [1]. A few studies from the 1980s and 1990s support the historical perception that the prevalence of vascular disease among American Indians and Alaskan Natives is lower than the rates found among Blacks and Whites in the United States [2,3]. However, the Strong Heart Study, a cohort study evaluating coronary artery disease (CAD) risk in selected American Indian communities in Arizona, Oklahoma, and North and South Dakota showed CAD mortality rates between 1984 and 1988 were twice as high among the Dakotan Indians compared with the rest of the United States' non-Native American population [4]. These findings are supported by a recent study comparing trends in CAD and stroke mortality between American Indians and Whites living in Montana between 1991 to 2000 [5]. Between 1991 and 1995 the age-adjusted CAD mortality rates per 100,000 people was 326 ± 36 in American Indian men compared with 308 ± 8 in White men and 239 ± 43 in American Indian women compared with 176 ± 5 in White women. In addition to having increased CAD risk, American Indians experienced a lesser decline in CAD mortality during the ensuing decade of follow-up: CAD mortality declined significantly among White men and women (from 237 ± 5 to 216 ± 4 per 100,00) but not significantly for American Indians (from 326 ± 36 to 283 ± 31 per 100,000).

The higher incidence of CAD risk among American Indians reflects a higher prevalence of CAD risk factors. Among 5,121 Native Americans living in Rhode Island, who are primarily members of the Narragansett Indian Tribe, CAD was approximately twice as great among the Indians and was the leading cause of death [6]. This finding is especially striking as the median age for the Indian population was 26.3 years compared to the overall state population of 36.7 years. Compared with the overall Rhode Island population twice as many American Indians in this survey smoked cigarettes and were obese. The prevalence of multiple CAD risk factors among American Indians and Alaska Natives was 47% in 2003 which is similar to the 49% prevalence found in Black Americans (another high risk population) [7]. The prevalence of having 2 or more CAD risk factors among American Indians living in Montana increased from 34% to 44% between 1999 and 2003 [8]. Although American Indians have a high prevalence of CAD risk factors significant variations in smoking rates and diabetes mellitus exist across different regions in the US [9]. The Strong Heart Study showed the prevalence of hypertension was 40% in American Indian inhabitants of Arizona and Oklahoma compared with 25% of those dwelling in the Dakotas yet approximately 50% of all groups received adequate blood pressure treatment [10]. Ten percent of Oklahoma- and Dakota-dwelling American Indians had plasma low density lipoprotein cholesterol levels > 160 mg/dL compared with 5% in Arizona. However all sites had a similarly high prevalence of obesity that was approximately 40% among men and 50% among women. The purpose of this discussion is to promote clinician awareness regarding overweight/obesity-related issues in Native Americans and emphasize the role of lifestyle interventions for reducing the prevalence of obesity in this population.

OVERWEIGHT/OBESITY IN NATIVE AMERICANS AND CAD RISK

Obesity in adults is defined as a BMI > 30 kg/m^2, and individuals with a BMI > 25 kg/m^2 are considered overweight. According to the latest National Health and Nutrition Examination Survey (NHANES), an estimated 131 million American adults are overweight or obese [11] and the prevalence of BMI > 30 kg/m^2 disproportionately higher in American Indians, Alaskan Natives, Native Hawaiians and Pacific Islanders [12,13]. Data from the Pathways Study in 1,704 American Indian children showed that 31% of girls and 27% of boys were greater than the 95th percentiles for BMI-for-age (i.e overweight); an additional 21% of girls and 20% of boys had a BMI-for-age that was in the 85th -95 percentiles. The national averages in nonnative American communities [14] showed 11% of 6- to 11-year –olds across the country have a BMI above the 95th percentile compared with 29% of Native American children in the Pathways study [15]. The increased prevalence of overweight/obesity (up 74% since 1991) is linked to increased risk for the Metabolic Syndrome (MetS). During the past 2 decades, the prevalence of the Metabolic Syndrome (MetS) in the US has progressively increased to the point regarded as 'epidemic' [16].

MetS was defined in 2001 according to the National Cholesterol Education Program (NCEP) Expert Panel as having 3 or more of the following conditions: 1. Abdominal obesity (waist circumference > 102 cm [40 inches] in men, > 88 cm [35 inches] in women), 2. Triglycerides ≥ 150 mg/dL, 3. Plasma high density lipoprotein (HDL)-cholesterol < 40 mg/dL in men, < 50 mg/dL in women, 4. Blood pressure elevation (≥130/≥85 mm Hg [or receiving anti-hypertensive therapy]), 5. Fasting plasma glucose > 110 mg/dL [17]. This is summarized in Table 1. Recently the threshold for plasma fasting plasma glucose has been lowered to > 100 mg/dL. [18].

Table 1. National Cholesterol Education Program Expert Panel's MetS Criteria is defined as having 3 or more of the following conditions

1. Abdominal obesity (waist circumference > 102 cm [40 inches] in men, > 88 cm [35 inches] in women).
2. Triglycerides ≥ 150 mg/dL
3. Plasma high density lipoprotein (HDL)-cholesterol < 40 mg/dL in men, < 50 mg/dL in women.
4. Blood pressure elevation (≥130/≥85 mm Hg [or receiving anti-hypertensive therapy]).
5. Fasting plasma glucose > 110 mg/dL (recent guidelines > 100 mg/dL).

The risk for MetS increases as a function of body adiposity [19,20]; specifically, increased body adiposity increases MetS risk [21]. Reaven [22] is recognized for his seminal work showing that a number of obesity-related metabolic disturbances reflecting increased CAD risk are associated with insulin resistance. These metabolic disturbances are clinically manifested as overlapping conditions that include insulin resistance, MetS, and Type 2 diabetes mellitus. MetS is associated with increased CAD risk [23,24]. A recent analysis of 6,447 men with CAD enrolled in the West of Scotland Coronary Prevention Study showed the presence of MetS at baseline predicted CAD events (Hazard Ratio = 1.30 [1.00 to 1.67]) in a multivariate model incorporating conventional CAD risk factors [23]. Men with 4 or 5 features of MetS had a 3.7-fold increased risk for CAD events than those with none. Similar findings have recently been reported in an analysis of lower risk populations [25], underscoring that MetS is associated with CAD risk that is not entirely accounted for by traditional CAD risk scoring paradigms.

LIFESTYLE AND OVERWEIGHT/OBESITY AMONG NATIVE AMERICANS

Obesity remains a complex and unresolved issue for Native Americans and other populations, even though the etiology of the disease is fundamentally simple. Weight gain results from an excessive consumption of energy that is not balanced by adequate energy expenditure (i.e. physical activity and exercise). The increased CAD risk among American Indians may reflect lifestyle changes that have occurred with their cultural fragmentation from traditional living situations to assuming a more urbanized existence characterized by *Luxus consumption* (i.e a high-fat, calorie-rich diet) coupled with sedentary behavior. The Pima Indians who have been subjects for numerous obesity studies are recognized as the prototype for this deleterious cultural transformation. Compared with Pima Indians living in Arizona who have high rates of obesity, those living a traditional lifestyle in Mexico do not [26].

DIETARY CONSIDERATIONS

Traditional Native American diets vary according to geographical locations but are generally low in animal fats and rich in fruits and vegetables. The Strong Heart Study has provided a detailed assessment of contemporary diet and physical activity among the American Indians groups studied in Arizona, Oklahoma and the Dakotas [10]. According to these findings, Native Americans counter-intuitively do not appear to consume excessive calories. The mean caloric consumption across the American Indian sites was approximately 2,000 kcals/day for men and 1,650 kcals/day for women. (NB. The average calorie allowance for a reference size man [170 lbs] over 51 years of age with light activity is 2,300 kcals/day and for a reference size woman [143 lbs] over 51 years of age with light activity is 1,900 kcals/day). However the average percent of fat (approximately 35% of calories from men and women across all American Indian sites) is greater than the currently NCEP recommended 30%. Similarly, the amount of dietary saturated fats consumed by American Indians exceeds NCEP guidelines. Animal products such as butter, lard, cheese, and beef fats are high in saturated fats as are coconut oil and palm oil which are used in bakery goods, processed foods, popcorn, oils, and nondairy creamers. This suggests that contemporary Native American diets are high in fats derived from animal products and commercially processed foods. Simple sugars, especially fructose, have been linked to increased risk for overweight/obesity [27]. Much of the increase in dietary fructose can be attributed to increased intakes of high-fructose beverages, such as soft drinks, juices, and juice drinks. An assessment of 'core foods' among Navajo 9- to 16-year olds shows the leading core food was soda (71% reporting frequent consumption) followed by fruit juices and French fries (67% of the children) [28]. These findings have been confirmed among Zuni children in New Mexico [29].

EXERCISE CONSIDERATIONS

Compared with the traditional Native American lifestyle that included regular participation in vigorous- and moderate-intensity levels of physical activity contemporary Native Americans live a much more sedentary lifestyle that increases their risk for overweight/obesity. Moreover fewer Native Americans participate in traditional physical activities such as drumming and ceremonial dancing. In a longitudinal study of 1,728 Pima Indians, Kriska et. al. [30] demonstrated that those with the highest levels of leisure time physical activity had the lowest incidence of becoming overweight and developing diabetes mellitus. Increased participation in leisure time physical activity of 30 to 60 minutes of moderate-intensity physical activity (such as walking) most days of the week is recommended to reduce the risk of overweight/obesity [31]. The Strong Heart Study found gardening, walking, and hunting were the most commonly reported leisure time physical activities among men who spent approximately 8 hours a week engaged in leisure time physical activity pursuits [10]. Women reported spending approximately 5 hours each week in leisure time physical activity, reporting walking, gardening, and dancing as the most popular items. Men were also involved in more work-related physical activity (12 hours per week) compared with women (8 hours per week). American Indians also reported watching television 3 hours per day which is less than the amount provided by the Neilson Report on television watching by people over the age of 54 years.

Current NCEP guidelines recommend long-term participation in therapeutic lifestyle change (TLC) weight loss programs of diet and physical exercise intervention for preventing and treating overweight/obesity and MetS [16]. The weight loss goal for reducing the risk for MetS and diabetes mellitus is approximately 7 percent of body weight (approximately 4 to 5 kilograms for most individuals). Although dietary interventions are a fundamental component of TLC programs aimed at weight reduction, physical activity and exercise play a pivotal role in reinforcing and sustaining long-term weight loss [32,33]. Maintaining changes in both dietary and exercise behaviors are important for improving long-term weight loss [34].

INTERVENTIONS FOR REDUCING OVERWEIGHT/OBESITY: A CLINICAL PERSPECTIVE

Combating overweight/obesity among Native Americans should occur at several levels. An important level involves public health awareness. In this regard it is important to recognize that Native Americans are disparately under-exposed to health messages and under represented in the media overall [35]. When Native Americans are included, they are often portrayed stereotypically (ie. the savage warrior, the alcoholic) [36]. Social marketing may be a key way to reach Native Americans with nutrition messages. Previous research with the Pima Indians has shown that a less direct and less structured intervention working through cultural and holistic principles is preferable to a direct and highly structured approach to modify diet and physical activity [37]. Using novel routes of communication that focus on healthier lifestyle choices among Native Americans is one strategy deserving further research.

The level of individual intervention is the domain of the clinician who needs to make an initial assessment of whether the 'patient' is interested and capable of participating in lifestyle change. The Health Belief Model [38] posits that people are more likely to take action if they believe that they are vulnerable or susceptible to the consequences of a behavior. Furthermore, people need to believe they are capable of changing their lifestyles and that these changes will lead to positive outcomes. Table 2. summarizes the four basic conditions for behavioral change. The Strong Heart Study showed that American Indians have good CAD risk factor knowledge with over 80 percent of men and women reporting awareness of the health risks of hypertension, hypercholesterolemia, overweight, sedentary behavior and cigarette smoking. This suggests that Condition I. and Condition II. are not limitations for the majority of Native Americans whereas Condition III. and Condition IV. may pose greater obstacles. For example, healthy food supplies and transportation are limited for many Native Americans due to the impoverished conditions in which many live may limit their ability and access to lifestyle change [36].

Table 2. Four Basic Conditions for Behavioral Change

i.   Awareness and understanding of information
ii. Awareness of potential benefit of change
iii. Individual feels able to perform activity or habit
iv. Accessible mode of change and supportive social environment.

Lifestyle programs can be classified according to different modalities of intervention. For the purposes of this discussion these programs are conceptualized simply as group- or individual-based interventions. Examples of successful group-based programs for TLC involving both weight loss through diet and physical activity have used center-based reinforcement sessions with dietary counseling initially administered on a weekly basis which then fade to lower intensity as the program progresses [32,39,40]. The Trial of Nonpharmacologic Interventions in the elderly (TONE), a randomized study in men and women aged 60 to 80 years, aimed at achieving and maintaining a 4.5 Kg. weight loss combined with dietary sodium restriction, exemplifies this approach [41]. Subjects receiving the lifestyle intervention met with nutrition and exercise counselors in individual and small group sessions on a regular basis and had a 4.7 Kg weight reduction after 30 weeks compared with the 0.9 Kg weight reduction in those receiving usual care.

Recently the Diabetes Prevention Program Research Group, considered as the 'gold standard' of group-based TLC programs, employed a 16-lesson center-based TLC program that administered a curriculum covering diet, exercise, and behavior in conjunction with a dietary and physical activity programs to help participants achieve and maintain their goal of a 7 percent weight loss [32] in a group of 3,234 non-diabetics who were at high-risk for diabetes mellitus. This study deliberately enrolled 50% of participants from ethnic minority populations including Blacks, Hispanic Americans, and Native Americans. The two major goals of the Diabetes Prevention Program lifestyle intervention were; i.) a minimum of 7% weight loss/weight maintenance and ii.) a minimum of 150 min/week of physical activity similar in intensity to brisk walking. The curriculum, taught by case managers in a face-to-face center-based venue was administered on a weekly basis for the first 8 weeks, biweekly for the next 16 weeks, then monthly for the remainder of the long-term intervention. Those receiving this center-based LTC intervention were more successful in sustaining weight loss and reduced their incidence of diabetes by 58% after a 3 year follow-up period compared with the non-intervention group. Many Native Americans, like many others, are unlikely to participate in long-term exercise programs due to such factors as inconvenience and the expense of frequent travel to their exercise sessions [42]. Because these programs are not typically available on a widespread basis, creating other means to provide these counseling sessions such as videos is an important consideration.

Although exercise guidelines indicate that practitioners should have an active role in promoting physical activity, health practitioners do not routinely counsel patients about physical activity in the usual care-wellness setting [43] and focus primarily on patients who are at high risk for disease [44]. The Activity Counseling Trial (ACT) was a multi-center trial that randomized 395 women and 479 men to receive i.) physician advice with educational materials, ii.) physician advice plus interactive mail and behavioral counseling assistance at physician visits, or iii.) physician advice and assistance plus regular investigator-initiated phone counseling and behavioral classes [45]. After 24 months women's physical fitness levels (measured as VO_{2max}) were greater in the assistance (group ii.) and the counseling (group iii.) groups than in the advice group (group i.) although no group differences in levels of self-reported physical activity were noted. No differences were noted among the groups of men for either physical fitness levels or self-reported physical activity. These findings indicate that exercise promotion when provided in the usual primary care setting may not be adequate to substantially affect long-term physical activity behaviors.

Although program-based TLC interventions can play an important role in reducing MetS, the role of the clinician to successfully impact TLC success through individualized counseling has been recently emphasized [46] despite the disappointing findings from the clinician-only intervention arm in ACT. The 33rd Bethesda Conference on Preventive Cardiology identified a need to understand the barriers to professional adherence to prevention guidelines at the community, provider, and patient levels [47]. The conference urged placing special focus on vulnerable groups, including Native Americans. A recent survey of medical residents and attending physicians in a large, urban public hospital identified 2 main barriers to effective prevention counseling: lack of training in prevention, and our health care system's emphasis on acute rather than preventive care [48].

In order to be successful the clinician must believe that the patient is capable of change, and must understand the 'ABCs' (i.e. attitude, beliefs, and core values) of the patient. Prior to TLC counseling it is paramount for a clinician to obtain information regarding the patient's lifestyle in order to tailor TLC counseling to the individual. Moreover a medical history and physical examination can identify patients with medical conditions that require rehabilitative exercise interventions. Suggesting one change at a time, i.e. single concept learning, may be more practical than trying to persuade patients to change their entire behavior pattern. According to Bandura's Social Learning Theory, behavior is learned and can be unlearned [49]. People learn most effectively when they are actively involved in the decision-making process and believe that they can change. The provider and patient should collaborate in developing a plan and setting goals for behavior change. Although individuals need adequate information on which to base a decision to change they must also believe in their own ability to make changes and must be encouraged to strive for positive outcomes. Individuals need the skills, support, and resources tailored to them. The goal for physical activity should be specific. Although current recommendations suggest 30 minutes of moderate intensity a day on at least 5 days a week, this recommendation may not seem meaningful to most patients. In this context a specific goal could be to 'take an evening stroll with the family'.

CONCLUSIONS

Native Americans are at increased risk for overweight/obesity and hence are at risk for increased CAD. Practitioners can take an active role in identifying high-risk patients and providing lifestyle interventions for weight reduction in this population.

ACKNOWLEDGEMENTS

The Authors wish to thank Jane E. Weinreb M.D for her expert comments regarding the manuscript.

REFERENCES

[1]   Smith SC, Clark LT, Cooper R, Daniels SR, Kumanyika SK, Ofili E, Quinones MA, Sanchez EJ, Saunders E, Tiukinhoy. AHA Conference Proceedings. Discovering the full spectrum of cardiovascular disease. Minority Health Summit 2003: Report of the Obesity, Metabolic Syndrome, and Hypertension Writing Group. *Circulation* 2005;111:e1134-e139).

[2]   Mensah GA, Mokdad AH, Ford ES, Greenlund KJ, Croft JB. State of disparities in cardiovascular health in the United States. *Circulation* 2005;111:1233-1241.

[3]   Gillum RF. The epidemiology of stroke in Native Americans. *Stroke* 1995;26:514-521.

[4]   Lee ET, Cowan LD, Welty TN, Sievers M, Howard WJ, Oopik A, Wang W, Yeh J, Devereux RB, Rhoades ER, Fabsitz RR, Go O, Howard BV. All-cause mortality and cardiovascular disease mortality in three American Indian populations, aged 45 to 74 years, 1984-1988. The Strong Heart Study. *Am J Epidemiol.* 1998;147:995-1008.

[5]   Harwell TS, Oser CS, Okon NJ, Fogle CC, Helgerson SD, Gohdes D.Defining disparities in cardiovascular disease for American Indians. Trends in heart disease and stroke MORTALITY among American Indians and Whites in Montana, 1991 to 2000. *CIRCULATION.* 2005;112:2263-2267.

[6]   62004 Minority Fact Sheet, The Office of Minority Health, Rhode Island Department of Health. 2004

[7]   Centers for Disease Control and Prevention. Racial/ethnic and socioeconomic disparities in multiple risk factors for heart disease and stroke-United States, 2003. *MMWR* 2005;54:113-117.

[8]   Oser CS, Harwell TS, Strasheim C, Fogle CC, Blades LL, Gohdes D, Helgerson SD. Trends in cardiovascular disease risk factors among American Indians in Montana. *AM J Prev Med* 2005;28:295-297.

[9]   Denny CH, Holtzman D, Cobb N. Surveillance of health behaviors of American Indians and Alaska Natives : findings from the Behavioral Risk Factor Surveillance System 1997-2000. *MMWR.* 2003;52:1-13.

[10] Strong Heart Study Data Book. US Department of Health and Human Services, *NIH publication* No.1-3285, Nov 2001.

[11] Mokdad AH, Bowman BA, Ford ES, Vinicor F, Marks JS, Koplan JP. The continuing epidemics of obesity and diabetes in the United States. *JAMA* 2001;286:1195-2000.

[12] American Indians/Alaska Natives and Cardiovascular Diseases. *Statistics Fact Sheet.* Dallas, Tex: American Heart Association 2004.

[13] *Asian/Pacific Islanders and Cardiovascular Diseases.* Statistics Fact Sheet. Dallas, Tex: American Heart Association 2004.

[14] Caballero B, Heims JH, Lohman T. Body composition and overweight prevalence in 1704 schoolchildren from 7 American Indian communities. *Am J Clin Nutr* 2003;78:308-312.

[15] Ogden CL, Flegal KM, Carroll MD, Johnson CL. Prevalence and trends in overweight among US children and adolescents. *JAMA* 2002;288:1728-1732.

[16] Flegal KM, Carroll MD, Ogden CL, Johnson CL. Prevalence and trends in obesity among US adults. *JAMA* 2003;289:76-79.

[17] Expert Panel on Detection, Evaluation, and Treatment of High Blood Cholesterol In Adults. Executive Summary Of The Third Report Of The National Cholesterol Education Program Expert Panel on Detection, Evaluation, and Treatment of High Blood Cholesterol in Adults. *JAMA* 2001;285:2486-2497.

[18] Fontbonne AM, Eschwege EM. Insulin and cardiovascular disease: Paris Prospective Study. *Diabetes Care* 1991;14:461-469.

[19] Ashton WD, Nanchahal K, Wood DA. Body mass index and metabolic risk factors for coronary heart disease in women. *Eur Heart J.* 2001;22:46-55.

[20] Haffner SM, Mykkanen L, Festa A, Burke J, Stern M. Insulin resistant pre-diabetic subjects have more atherogenic risk factors than insulin sensitive pre-diabetic subjects: implications for preventing coronary heart disease during the pre-diabetic state. *Circulation* 2000;101:975-980.

[21] Reaven GN. Role of insulin resistance in human disease. Diabetes 1988;37:1596-1607.

[22] Sattar N, Gaw A, Scherbakova O, et. al. Metabolic syndrome with and without C-reactive protein as a predictor of coronary heart disease and diabetes in the West of Scotland Coronary Prevention Study. *CIRC* 2003;108:414-419.

[23] Girman CJ, Rhodes T, Mercuri M, et. al. The metabolic syndrome and risk of major events in the Scandanavian Simvastatin Survival Study (4S) and the Air Force/Texas Coronary Atherosclerosis Prevention Study (AFCAPS/TexCAPS). *Am J Cardiol* 2004;93:136-141.

[24] HuG, Quiao Q, Tuomilehto J, Balkau B, Borch-Johnsen K, and Pyorala K. Prevalence of the metabolic syndrome and its relation to all-cause and cardiovascular mortality in nondiabetic European men and women. *Arch Intern Med* 2004;164:1066-1076.

[25] Ravussin E, Valencia ME, Esparza J, BennettPH, Schultz LO. Effects of a traditional lifestyle on obesity in Pima Indians. *Diabetes Care* 1994;17:1067-1074.

[26] Enidt SS, Kein NC, Stern JS, Teff K, Havel PJ. Fructose, weight gain, and the insulin resistance syndrome. *Am J CLIN Nutr* 2002;76:911-922.

[27] Koehler KM, Harris MB, Davis SM. Core, secondary, and peripheral foods in the diets of Hispanic, Navajo, and Jemez Indian children. *J Am Diet ASSOC* 1989;89:538-540.

[28] Cole SM, Teufel-shone NI, Ritenbaugh CK, Yzenbaard RA, Cockerham DL. Dietary intake and food patterns of Zuni adolescents. *J Am Diet ASSOC* 2001;101:131-142.).

[29] Kriska AM, Saremi A, Hanson RL, Bennett P, Kobes S, Wiulliam D, Knowler W. Physical activity, obesity, and the incidence of type 2 diabetes in a high-risk population. *Am J Epidmiol* 2003;158:669-67

[30] Pate RR, Pratt M, Blair SN, Thompson PD, Paffenbarger RS, DeBusk RF. Physical activity and public health. A recommendation from the Centers for Disease Control and Prevention and the American College of Sports Medicine. *JAMA* 1995;273:402-407.

[31] Diabetes Prevention Program Research Group. Reduction in the incidence of type 2 diabetes with lifestyle intervention or metformin. *N Eng J Med* 2002;346:393-403.

[32] Jakicic JM, Marcus BH, Gallagher KI, Napolitano M, Lang W. Effect of exercise duration and intensity on weight loss in overweight, sedentary women. *JAMA* 2003;290:1323-1330.

[33] Hu G, Lindstrom J, Valle T, Eriksson JG, Jousilahti P, Silventoinen K, Qiao Q, Tuomilehto J. Physical activity, body mass index, and risk of Type 2 diabetes in patients with normal or impaired glucose regulation. *Arch Intern Med* 2004;164:892-896.

[34] Larson MS. Race and interracial relationships in children's television commercials. *Howard J. Comm* 2002;13:223-235.

[35] Alaniz ML, Wilkes C. Pro-drinking messages and message environments for young adults: the case of alcohol industry advertising in African American, Latino, and Native American communities. *J Public Health Policy.* 1998;19:447-472.

[36] Narayan KMV, Hoskin M, Kozak D. Randomized clinical trial of lifestyle intervention in Pima Indians; a pilot study. *Diabet Med* 1998;15:66-72.

[37] Rosenstock I. In Glanz K, et. al., eds. *Health Behavior and Education: Theory, Research and Practice.* San Francisco: Jossey-Bass, 1990.

[38] Ard JD, Grambow SC, Liu D, Slentz CA, Kras WE, Svetkey PL. The effect of the PREMIER interventions on insulin sensitivity. *Diabetes Care* 2004;27:340-347.

[39] Dubbert PM, Cooper KM, Kirchner KK, Meydrech EM, and Bilbrew D. Effects of nurse counseling on walking for exercise in elderly primary care patients. *Journal of Gerontology: Medical Sciences* 2002;57A:M733-M740.

[40] Whelton PK, Appel LJ, Espeland MA, et. al. Sodium reduction and weight loss in the treatment of hypertension in older persons. A randomized

controlled trial of Nonpharmacologic Interventions in the Elderly (TONE). *JAMA* 1998;279:839-846.

[41] Marcus BH, Dubbert PM, Forsyth LH, McKenzie TL, Stone EJ, Dunn AL, Blair SN. Physical activity behavior change: Issues in adoption and maintenance. *HEALTH PSYCHOLGY* 2000;19(1,S):32-41.

[42] Wee McCarthy EP, David RB, Phillips RS. Physician counseling about exercise. *JAMA* 1999;282:1583-1588.

[43] Wells KB, et. al. The practices of general and subspecialty internists in counseling about smoking and exercise. *Am J Pub Health* 1986;76:1009-1013.

[44] The Writing Group of the ACT Research Group. The effects of physical activity counseling in primary care. The ACTS: A randomized control trial. *JAMA* 2001;286:677-687.

[45] Manson JE, Skerret PJ, Greenland, Van Itallie TB. The escalating pandemics of obesity and sedentary lifestyle. A call to action for clinicians. *Arch Intern Med* 2004;164:249-258.

[46] Aedes PA, Kottke TE, Miller NH, et. al. Task Force #3 – Getting results: who where, how? *J Am Coll Cardiol* 2002;40:615-629.

[47] Tsui JI, Dodson K, Jacobson TA. Cardiovascular disease prevention counseling in residency: resident and attending physician attitudes and practices. *J Natl Med Assoc* 2004;96:1080-1091.

[48] Bandura A. *Social foundations of thought and action: a social cognitive theory.* Englewood Cliffs, NJ: Prentice-Hall, 1986.

In: Exercise and Health Research ISBN: 978-1-60021-985-6
Editor: M. D. Johansen, pp. 137-155 © 2008 Nova Science Publishers, Inc.

Chapter 6

EFFECTS OF PHYSICAL EXERCISE WITH A DIETARY VITAMINS C AND E COMBINATION ON OXIDATIVE STRESS IN MUSCLE, LIVER AND BRAIN OF STREPTOZOTOCIN- INDUCED DIABETIC PREGNANT RAT

*Mustafa Nazıroğlu**
Department of Biophysics, Medical Faculty, Süleyman Demirel University,
TR-32260, Isparta, Turkey

ABSTRACT

  The responses to oxidative stress induced by diabetes may be change in the brain, liver and muscle. Moderate physical exercise with vitamins C and E (VCE) supplementation can be beneficial to diabetes due to reducing free radical production in the tissues of diabetic pregnant rats. I investigated the effect of VCE supplementation and physical moderate exercise on lipid peroxidation and antioxidant levels in the muscle, liver and brain of STZ-induced diabetic pregnant rats.

---

* Corresponding address: Prof. Dr. Mustafa Naziroğlu; Department of Biophysics, Medical (TIP) Faculty, Süleyman Demirel University, Posta kutusu 68; TR-32260, Cünür, Isparta, Turkey. Tel: +90 246 2113310; Fax: +90 246 2371165; E-mail: mnaziroglu@med.sdu.edu.tr

Fifty female Wistar rats were used and were randomly divided into five groups. First and second were used as the control and pregnant control group. Third group was the pregnant diabetic group. The fourth group was the diabetic-pregnant-exercise group. VCE- supplemented feed was given to pregnant-diabetic-exercise rats constituting the fifth group. Animals in the exercised groups were moderately exercised daily on a treadmill (16.1 m/min, 45 min/d) for three weeks (five days a week). Diabetes was induced on day zero of the study before mating animals. Muscle, liver and brain samples were taken from all animals on day 20.

Exercise and administration of VCE to pregnant diabetic rats resulted in significant decrease in the glutathione peroxidase (GSH-Px), reduced glutathione (GSH), vitamin E and β- carotene levels and the elevated lipid peroxidation levels. The values in the muscle were most affected by diabetes. Exercise in the diabetic pregnant group did not change GSH and vitamin E levels in the brain although lipid peroxidation levels in the liver, muscle and brain decreased. In the diabetic pregnant animals, the decreased β- carotene, vitamins A and E concentration and GSH and GSH-Px levels in muscle and liver did not improve through exercise only although their concentrations were increased by VCE supplementation.

In conclusion, our results suggest that responses of the brain to oxidative stress by diabetes are quite different from those in liver and muscle. There was he beneficial effect of exercise with a dietary VCE on investigated antioxidant defenses and tissue lipid peroxidation in the muscle and liver of the diabetic- pregnant rat model. The moderate exercise training with a VCE supplementation may play a role in preventing diabetic muscle and liver diseases of diabetic pregnant animals.

Keywords: Oxidative stress; Diabetes; Physical Exercise; Pregnancy; Vitamin C and E; Muscle

ABBREVIATIONS

GSH,   reduced glutathione
GSH-Px,   glutathione peroxidase
PDEx,   pregnant diabetic and exercised group.
PDExCE,   vitamin C and E supplemented group
ROS,   reactive oxygen species
SOD,   superoxide dismutase

STZ,   streptozotocin
VCE,   vitamin C and E combination

INTRODUCTION

Pregnancy complicated by poorly controlled diabetes is associated with an increased risk of abortion, congenital malformations, muscle and liver degeneration [Nazıroğlu and Çay, 2001; Damasceno et al., 2002]. Although numerous studies on the causes of diabetes have been carried out, the causes and mechanisms involved are still unclear. Recently, several workers suggested that increased production of reactive oxygen species (ROS), such as superoxide anion and hydrogen peroxide, are implicated in the pathogenesis of diabetes and cause various complications of diabetes, such as liver and muscle degeneration [Nazıroğlu and Çay, 2001; Viana et al., 2003]. Excess ROS accelerates oxidative damage to DNA and other molecules, such as proteins and lipids [Kinalski et al., 1999; Kedziora-Kornatowska et al., 2003]. Furthermore, increased glucose concentrations increase oxidative stress through the production of mitochondrial ROS, nonenzymatic glycation of proteins, and glucose autooxidation [Siman and Eriksson, 1997a and b; Kedziora-Kornatowska et al., 2003]. Recent studies have demonstrated that exposure to high glucose concentrations increases the levels of ROS in the plasma of rat streptozotocin (STZ) induced pregnant diabetes [Damasceno et al., 2002; Nazıroğlu et al. 2004; Kutlu et al. 2005]. However, there are also some reports showing that exercise fails to result a functinally significant level of oxidative stress in the muscle [Takanami et al. 2000; Liu et al. 2000; Atalay and Laaksonen, 2002; Lee et al., 2002]. Thus far, the evidence for tissue oxidative stress and damage due to exercise remains incomplete because of the complexity of exercise models. We still lack a comprehensive picture regarding the relationship between oxidative stress and exercise in the brain, liver and muscles.

Brain and muscles are consuming the highest amount of oxygen in human body. Although most of the oxygen used in brain and muscle converted to CO_2 and water, some little of oxygen forms ROS. The existences of polyunsaturated fatty acids which are targets of those of the ROS in brain make this organ more sensitive to oxidative damage [Liu et al., 2000]. Therefore, there are various antioxidant mechanisms in brain and muscle neutralizing harmful effects of ROS yet with diabetes the lose of efficiency of antioxidants mechanisms and the alterations in the electron transfer chain in mitochondria increase the free radical formation due to hypermetabolism and glucose autooxidation.

In diabetic patient and animals, lower activity of key antioxidant enzymes, such as superoxide dismutase (SOD) and glutathione peroxidase (GSH-Px), was observed [Kedziora-Kornatowska et al., 2003; Nazıroğlu et al., 2004b]. Studies of numerous authors indicated favorable effects observed after vitamin E or vitamin C supplementation in the blood of pregnant diabetic animals [Siman and Eriksson, 1997a and b; Kinalski et al., 1999; Damasceno et al., 2002; Kedziora-Kornatowska et al., 2003; Nazıroğlu et al., 2004a]. However, so far there haven't been reported in regards to antioxidant effectiveness in the hazard of diabetic muscle and liver degeneration in pregnant and exercised animals. Studies, focused on the antioxidant levels and lipid peroxidation, are required to prove VCE combination therapeutic usefulness in diabetic pregnant rats.

The most frequently studied antioxidant vitamins are vitamins C and E (VCE). The VCE have been administrated separately in studies in which they were given orally to pregnant diabetic rats, yielding a decrease in the oxidative stress [Siman and Eriksson, 1997a and b; Kinalski et al., 1999). Vitamin E is a lipophilic antioxidant interfering with the chain reaction of lipid peroxidations and much attention has been paid to whether vitamin E improves athletic performance [Takanami et al. 2000]. Furthermore, the preventive effect of vitamin E on exercise- induced oxidative damage has also been demonstrated [Meydani et al. 1993; Şimşek et al. 2005; Kutlu et al. 2005; Nazıroğlu and Butterworth, 2005]. It should help us to perform endurance exercise without serious risk damage, and thus give us the advantage of being able to prevent degenerative diseases through aerobic exercise without incurring other health disorders. Vitamin C is a hydrophilic molecule that can scavenge several radicals, among them the hydroxyl radical. It is likely that VCE act in a synergistic manner, by vitamin E primarily being oxidized to the tocopheroxyl radical and then reduced back to tocopherol by vitamin C [Packer and Landvik, 1990; Czernichow and Hercberg, 2001]. In contrast to vitamin A, the VCE combination can also be safely used in high doses in the prevention of diseases such as diabetes and cardiovascular disease [Packer and Landvik, 1990; Czernichow and Hercberg, 2001; Nazıroğlu M, Çay, 2001; Nazıroğlu et al., 2004a]. Against this back ground we decided to use the lipophilic antioxidant vitamin E and the hydrophilic antioxidant vitamin C together as antioxidative protection in our rat model for STZ- induced radical production.

Although there have been many studies on oxidative stress caused by diabetes and exercise that utilized oxidative biomarkers in various tissues, especially muscle, many questions still remain unanswered, such as 1) does exercise cause oxidative stress in organs, such as brain and liver other than muscle of pregnant diabetic rats?; 2) does moderate exercise show different effects on oxidative stress in various organs of pregnant diabetic rats? 3) What is the relationship between diabetes/exercise- induced oxidative stress and antioxidants? and 4) What is the protective effects of VCE combination on oxidative stress in various organs of pregnant rats? We hypothesize that moderate exercise with a dietary VCE combination may have important effects on organs such as brains well as muscle and liver and that antioxidants may play an impotent role in the adaptation to exercise induced oxidative stress in these organs.

If diabetes increases lipid peroxidation, increased amounts of enzymatic and non-enzymatic antioxidants should be oxidized and their levels in muscle, liver and brain should be diminished. Thus, the aim of the study is to assess selected parameters of oxidative stress in pregnant rat muscle, brain and liver in the course of STZ- induced diabetes as well as the effect of exercise with VCE on pro- and antioxidative processes in the organs of the investigated animals *in vivo*.

MATERIALS AND METHODS

Chemicals

All chemicals were obtained from Sigma Chemical Inc. (St. Louis, MO, USA) and all organic solvents from Merck Chemical Inc. (Darmstadt, Germany) except vitamin C and E. The oral form of vitamin C (ascorbic acid) and vitamin E (dl-α-tocopheryl acetate) was obtained from F. Hoffman La Roche (İstanbul, Turkey). STZ was obtained from SERVA GmbH (Heidelberg, Germany). All reagents were analytical grade. All reagents except the phosphate buffers were prepared each day and stored in a refrigerator at + 4 °C. The reagents were equilibrated at room temperature for 0.5 h before use when the analysis was initiated or reagents containers were refilled. Phosphate buffers were stable at +4 °C for 1 month.

Animals and Diets

The Medical Faculty Experimentation Ethics Committee of our university approved the experimental procedures of the study. Non-pregnant animals and those that died due to diabetes were removed from the study. At the beginning of the main study, ten female and forty pregnant Wistar rats bred in our laboratory were used. Housing was at 22-24°C with light from 08.00 to 20.00 with free access to water. At the start of the experiment the rats were 12 weeks old and weighed 150-165 g. They were randomly distributed into five groups and housed individually in stainless-steel cages in a pathogen-free University Laboratory Animal Research facility. All animals were fed a commercial diet (Elazığ Feed Factory, Elazığ, Turkey) including the ingredients shown in Table 1 during the experiment. VCE supplemented and unsupplemented feed compositions were homogenized by using a mixer and pellets were prepared in our laboratory by heating below 45°C for 2 days. The VCE supplemented diet contained an ascorbic acid (1 g) and dl-α-tocopheryl acetate (600 mg) combination per kg feed.

Table 1. Diet composition

Ingredients	%
Corn	25.1
Barley	20.2
Soybean	36.0
Wheat	9.7
Fish flour	3.2
Meat-bone flour	2.4
Calcium-phosphate	1.7
Salt	1.1
Methionine	0.2
Lysin	0.2
Vitamin / mineral mix*	0.2

* In per kg mixture: Vitamin A 12.000.000 IU; vitamin C 50 mg; vitamin D_3 400 000 IU; vitamin E 30 mg; vitamin K_3 2.5 mg and vitamins B_1 3 mg; B_2 7 mg; B_6 4 mg and B_{12} 15 mg; nicotinamide 4 mg; calcium-D pantothane 8 mg; Folic acid 1 mg; biotin 45 mg; folic acid 1 mg; Mn 80 mg; Fe 40 mg; Zn 60 mg; Cu 5 mg; I 0.4 mg; Co 0.1 mg; Se 0.15 mg and antioxidant (Butyhydroxytoluol) 10 mg.

Induction of Pregnancy and Diabetes

After 2 weeks acclimatization, diabetes was induced in female rats with STZ using a previously described method [Nazıroğlu and Çay, 2001]. STZ was intraperitoneally (i.p.) administered at a dose of 40 mg/kg body weight dissolved in citrate buffer (0.1 M, pH 4.5). Control rats received i.p. citrate buffer. Blood glucose was measured 10 days after induction of diabetes. Diabetes was defined as a blood glucose concentration >20 mM. The female rats were mated overnight with non-diabetic male rats 10 days after STZ or citrate buffer injection. The morning when sperm was found in the vaginal smear was designated gestational day zero.

Exercise Program

Treadmill speed and duration of exercise were gradually increased until at 14 days the rats were running at a speed of 16.1 m/min for 15 min. By day 14, speed was held constant at 16.1 m/min and animals ran 45 min/day as described by Uriu-Hare et al. [1989]. This level of exercise was maintained from gestational day zero until the end of the 20- day. This exercise intensity provides a mild to moderate aerobic stress for animals [Uriu-Hare et al., 1989]. Animals not complying with the adaptation protocol were removed from study. The non-exercising group remained sedentary during this time period but was exposed to the same environmental conditions as the runners during the training sessions. All exercise sessions were conducted during each animal's dark cycle. The animals in the sedentary groups had no access to food and water during the time period corresponding to the exercise bouts.

Study Groups and Sampling

The female rats were mated overnight with non-diabetic male rats 10 days after STZ or citrate buffer injection. The morning on which sperm were found in the vaginal smear was designated gestational day 0. This experimental study was composed of five groups: the first and second were used as control and pregnant control groups. The third group was the pregnant diabetic (DP) group. The fourth was used as the diabetic-pregnant-exercise (DPEx) group. VCE was supplemented to pregnant-diabetic-exercise (DPExCE) rats in the fifth group during gestational days. All animals wew fasted for 12 h before death. On day 20 of pregnancy, the rats were anaesthetized with ether for 5 minutes.

Preparation of Tissue Samples

The brain, liver and vastus lateralis muscles from both hind legs (subdivided into fast and slow muscle groups) were sampled. These are the muscles most widely studied although these muscles may not be representative of the whole body. The tissues were removed from all animals in the same order; liver, brain and leg muscles. The tissues were immediately covered by ice- cold buffer and kept on ice and the immediately transported to a cold room where they were processed to small preparations. The samples were stored at -30 $^\circ$C for < 3 months pending measurement of enzymatic activity. Half part of the samples was used for immediate lipid peroxidation and vitamin assay.

For the enzymatic analyses in liver, muscle and brain (80-100 mg) tissues were minced on a glass and homogenized by a glass-glass homogenizator (Çalıskan glass technique, Ankara, Turkey) in cold physiological saline on ice. Then the tissues were diluted with a nine-fold volume of phosphate buffer (pH 7.4).

Lipid Peroxidation Assay

Lipid peroxidation levels in liver, brain and muscle homogenate were measured with the thiobarbituric-acid reaction by the method of Placer et al. [1966] as described in previous studies [Nazıroğlu and Çay, 2001; Nazıroğlu et al., 2004a]. The quantification of thiobarbituric acid reactive substances was determined by comparing the absorption to the standard curve of malondialdehyde equivalents generated by acid catalyzed hydrolysis of 1,1,3,3 tetramethoxypropane. The values of lipid peroxidation were expressed as μmol/ g protein. In the current study we used the thiobarbituric-acid reaction method for determination of lipid peroxidation. Although the method is not specific for lipid peroxidation, measurement of thiobarbituric-acid reaction is an easy and reliable method, which is used as an indicator of lipid peroxidation and ROS activity in biological samples.

Reduced Glutathione (GSH), Glutathione Peroxidase (GSH-Px) and Protein Assay

The GSH content of the liver, brain and muscle homogenate was measured at 412 nm using the method of Sedlak and Lindsay [1968] as described own studies [Nazıroğlu, 2003; Nazıroğlu et al., 2004b]. The samples were precipitated with 50% trichloracetic acid and then centrifuged at 1000 g for 5 min. The reaction mixture contained 0.5 ml of supernatant, 2.0 ml of Tris-EDTA buffer (0.2 M; pH 8.9) and 0.1 ml of 0.01 M 5,5'-dithio-bis-2-nitrobenzoic acid. The solution was kept at room temperature for 5 min, and then read at 412 nm on the spectrophotometer. GSH-Px activities of the liver, muscle and brain were measured spectrophotometrically at 37 °C and 412 nm according to the Lawrence and Burk [1976].

The protein content in the liver, muscle and brain was measured by method of Lowry et al. [1951] with bovine serum albumin as the standard.

Plasma Vitamins A and E and β- Carotene Analyses

Vitamins A (retinol) and E (α-tocopherol) were determined in the liver, brain and muscle homogenates by a modification of the method described by Desai [1984]. Around of the fifty mg of muscle and liver samples were saponified by the addition of 0.3 ml 60 percent (w/v in water) KOH and two ml of one percent (w/v in ethanol) ascorbic acid, followed by heating at 70°C for 30 min. After cooling the samples on ice, 2 ml of water and 1 ml of n-hexane were added and mixed with the samples and then rested for 10 min to allow phase separation. N-hexane extract was dried under nitrogen at 40 °C and redissolved using 0.2 ml methanol. Twenty microliter portions of the methanol extracts were chromatographed on high-performance liquid chromatography. Fluorimetric detection of vitamin A used excitation and emission wavelengths of 330 and 480 nm, respectively. The relevant wavelengths for α-tocopherol detection were 292 and 330 nm. Calibration was performed using standard solutions of all-trans retinol and α-tocopherol in methanol.

The levels of β-carotene in liver and muscle samples were determined according to method of Suzuki and Katoh [1990]. Two milliliters of hexane were mixed with 50 mg liver and 100 mg muscle. The value of β- carotene in hexane was measured at 453 nm in the spectrophotometer.

Statistical Analyses

All results are expressed as means ±SD. To determine the effect of treatment, data were analyzed using one-way ANOVA repeated measures. P-values of less than 0.05 were regarded as significant. Significant values were assessed with Tukey's multiple range test. Data was analyzed using the SPSS statistical program (version 10.0 software, SPSS Inc. Chicago, Illinois, USA).

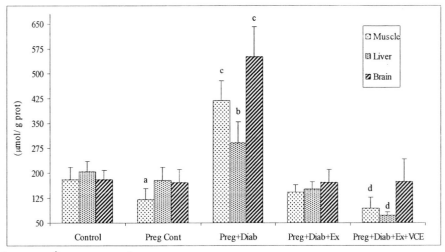

ᵃ p<0.05, ᵇ p<0.01 and ᶜ p<0.001 vs group control or preg. cont d p<0.05 vs group Preg+Diab+Ex

Figure 1. The effects of exercise and vitamin C and E (VCE) supplementation on lipid peroxidation (LP) levels in the muscle, liver and brain of diabetic pregnant rats. (mean ± SD, n=10).

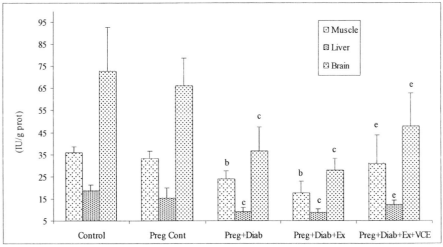

ᵇ p<0.01 and ᶜ p<0.001 vs group control or preg. cont. ᵉ p<0.01 vs group Preg+Ex.

Figure 2. The effects of exercise and vitamin C and E (VCE) supplementation on glutathione peroxidase (GSH-Px) levels in the muscle, liver and brain of diabetic pregnant rats. (mean ± SD, n=10).

RESULTS

Changes of Lipid Peroxidation Levels in the Brain, Liver and Muscles

The lipid peroxidation in the brain, liver and muscles are shown in Figure 1. The diabetes induced significant increases in lipid peroxidation levels in the brain, liver and muscles. When compared to control and pregnant control groups lipid peroxidation levels in the muscles, brain ($p < 0.001$) and liver ($p < 0.01$) were significantly higher in PD group. On the other hand, 20 days of both exercise and exercise plus VCE supplementation ($p < 0.05$) was caused a fall in the lipid peroxidation level of liver, muscle and brain.

Recent studies have indicated that high glucose levels cause oxidative stress [Kedziora-Kornatowska et al., 2003; Nazıroğlu et al., 2004b]. Glucose itself and the glycosylated proteins known as Amadori rearrangement products are susceptible to autooxidation and may be a source of ROS [Lee et al., 2002]. Furthermore, enhanced oxidative stress due to diabetes may also result from a dysfunction in the defense system against free radicals, such as reduction of GSH, β- carotene and vitamin E or inactivation of GSH-Px [Yadav et al., 1997; Siman and Eriksson, 1997a and b; Kinalski et al., 1999; Damasceno et al., 2002; Kedziora-Kornatowska et al., 2003; Nazıroğlu et al., 2004a]. Moderate physical exercise decreases the lipid peroxidation levels in brain, liver and muscle, indicating a possible beneficial effect of moderate physical exercise and VCE supplementation on brain, liver and muscle function. The increase in antioxidant β- carotene, GSH-Px, vitamins A and E may contribute to a decrease in brain, liver and muscle mitochondrial lipid peroxidation. It is possible that the increased oxidative stress may also cause mitochondrial genesis during stress [Liu et al., 2000].

Changes of Antioxidative Enzymes Values in the Brain, Liver and Muscles

The GSH-Px activity and GSH levels in the brain, liver and muscles were affected by either diabetes or exercise. The GSH levels ($p < 0.05$) in the liver and muscle and GSH-Px activity in the muscle ($p < 0.01$), liver and brain ($p < 0.001$) were significantly lower in the PD groups than in the control and pregnant control groups. The GSH-Px activity and GSH levels concentration in the tissues did not affect through exercise only. The GSH-Px activities in the brain, liver and muscles were significantly ($p<0.01$) higher in the PDExCE group than in the PDEx group. GSH levels in muscle ($p<0.01$) and liver ($p<0.05$) were significantly higher in the PDExCE group than in the PDEx group although the value in brain did not affect. Liver mean weights were between 6.31-8.71 g in five groups and they were not statistically different in exercise and VCE supplemented groups.

One of the most important intracellular antioxidant systems is the glutathione redox cycle. Glutathione is one of the essential compounds for maintaining cell integrity because of its reducing properties and participation in the cell metabolism [Halliwell and Gutteridge, 1999]. The exact mechanisms of the diabetes- induced changes in the liver and muscle GSH concentrations are not completely elucidated. Thus, glutathione may modulate metal reduction, and the thiol portion is very reactive with several chemical compounds, mainly with alkylating agents such as STZ and alloxan [Yadav et al., 1997; Lin, 1997]. On the other word, this may be due to the fact that diabetes causes a significant decrease in cysteine and cystine in the liver because cysteine is the rate- limiting precursor for glutathione synthesis. In this study, the decrease in the GSH concentration in liver and muscle as a result of diabetes may account for the increased lipid peroxidation. We have found that lipid peroxidation was levels are negatively correlated with GSH in the diabetes (data not shown). These findings are similar to results of other investigators studying GSH in relation to risk factors in diabetic subjects and animals [Kinalski et al., 1999; Kedziora-Kornatowska et al., 2003; Lee et al., 2002; Nazıroğlu et al., 2004b; Kutlu et al., 2004; Nazıroğlu and Butterworth, 2005].

Our data were not consistent with those from our previous blood, lens and kidney studies reporting increased GSH-Px activity in exercise and diabetic group [Şimşek et al. 2005, Kutlu et al., 2005]. GSH-Px is the main enzyme of the enzymatic antioxidant defense system responsible for protection against the increase in ROS production. Hydrogen peroxide formed by the catalytic reaction of SOD is both a reactive form of oxygen and a normal cellular metabolite, and it is further detoxified by GSH-Px and catalase [Halliwell and Gutteridge, 1999]. GSH-Px activities are reduced in the DP and DPEx groups. The reduced activities of GSH-Px could be due to its depletion or inhibition as a result of the increased production of free radicals. Hypoinsulinemia increases the activity of the fatty acylCO oxidase that initiates β-oxidation of fatty acids, resulting in the production of hydrogen peroxide, which detoxifies catalase and GSH-Px [Viana et al., 2003].

The brain utilizes %20 of total oxygen consumed by the whole body at rest. The oxygen consumption rate increases 10- to 15- fold exercise; however, the brain oxygen consumption is known to be constant during exercise [Liu et al.

2000]. Thus it is unlikely that exercise poses an oxidative stress to brain. The lack of oxidative stress to brain during exercise is noteworthy because the brain could be susceptible to lipid peroxidation damage due to high concentration of polyunsaturated fatty acids and lower levels of antioxidant enzymes (GSH- Px and catalase) and GSH. Diabetes and exercise did not cause decrease in the levels of GSH-Px and GSH in the brain. Moderate exercise and VCE supplementation caused an increase in the levels of GSH-Px, β- carotene, vitamins A and E which would help to protect the brain from oxidative damage.

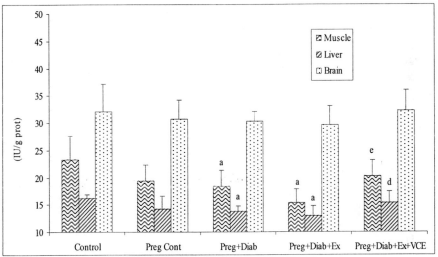

^{a}p<0.05 vs group control or preg. cont. ^{d} p<0.05 and ^{e} p<0.01 vs group Preg+Diab+Ex.

Figure 3. The effects of exercise and vitamin C and E (VCE) supplementation on reduced glutathione (GSH) levels in muscle, liver and brain of diabetic pregnant rats. (mean ± SD, n=10).

Changes of Antioxidative Vitamins Values in the Brain, Liver and Muscles

The changes in the β- carotene, vitamins A and E concentrations in the brain, liver and muscles are shown in Figures 4-6. Diabetes and exercise were associated with changes in β- carotene, vitamins A and E concentrations in the brain, liver and muscles samples. The vitamin E concentrations in the liver (p<0.001) and muscle (p<0.05), β- carotene concentrations in muscle (p<0.001) and liver (p<0.01) and vitamin A concentrations in the muscle samples (p<0.01) were significantly lower in the PD group than in the control and pregnant control groups. The β– carotene and vitamin A concentrations did not affect through exercise only. The vitamins A and E and β– coretene concentrations in the muscle and liver were positively affected by exercise plus VCE supplementation. The β– carotene in muscle (p<0.01) and liver (p<0.001), vitamins A in liver and muscle (p<0.01) and vitamin E in brain (p<0.05), liver and muscle (p<0.01) concentrations were significantly higher in the PDExCE group than in the PDEx group.

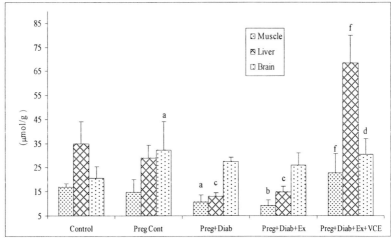

a p<0.05, b p<0.01 and c p<0.001 vs group control or preg Cont. d p<0.05 and f p<0.001 vs group Preg+Diab+Ex.

Figure 4. The effects of exercise and vitamin C and E (VCE) supplementation on vitamin E concentration in the muscle, liver and brain of diabetic pregnant rats. (mean ± SD, n=10).

Oxidative damage can cause irreversible cell damage through the loss of homeostasis functioning and the loss of mitochondria. However, the initiation of oxidative damage due to diabetes can be reversed by the stimulation of antioxidant enzymes, by maintaining an adequate concentration of intracellular antioxidants, and by repair systems. The increase in the levels of antioxidants leads to the scavenging of excess free radicals and thereby may contribute to a decrease in oxidative damage, whereas a decrease in the levels of antioxidants should lead to an increase in oxidative damage. There have been reports on the effect of exercise on vitamin E concentrations. While Meydani et al. [1993] and Mastaloudis et al. [2001] have reported increased vitamin E concentrations during or shortly after exercise, many investigations on human and animal models have shown decreased serum and muscle vitamin E concentration in chronic and acute exercise [Bowles et al., 1991; Liu et al. 2000]. The decrease in muscle vitamin E concentration in animals during exercise has been attributed to the generation of free radicals and lipid peroxidation [Takanami et al., 2000]. In the present experimental model, plasma vitamin E concentrations were significantly depleted via diabetes. Our results are in accordance with the comments of Bowles et al. [1991] and Liu et al. [2000].

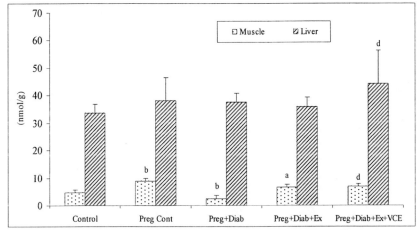

^{a} p<0.05, ^{b} p<0.01 and ^{c} p<0.001 vs group control or preg Cont. ^{d} p<0.05 vs group Preg+Diab+Ex.

Figure 5. The effects of exercise and vitamin C and E (VCE) supplementation on vitamin A concentration in the muscle and liver of diabetic pregnant rats. (mean ± SD, n=10).

Vitamin E in the brain, β− carotene and vitamin A levels in muscle were increased by pregnancy and the values were higher in the pregnant control group than in control group (p<0.05 and p<0.01) although lipid peroxidation level in muscle decreased (p<0.05). As its known, oestradiol concentrations in pregnancy were higher than in before pregnancy. A lot of studies [Akova et al., 2001; Nazıroğlu et al., 2004b] reported that oestradiol had antioxidant properties, even higher than in the antioxidant effect of vitamin E. Vanheest and Rodgers [1997] and Radak et al. [1999] have suggested that female rats may be relatively well protected against exercise induced oxidative stress even in vitamin E deficient conditions, possibly due to higher oestrogen concentrations. The results of the current study supported further role to the antioxidant role of oestrogen in pregnancy, as it is supplies a better protection against oxidative stress.

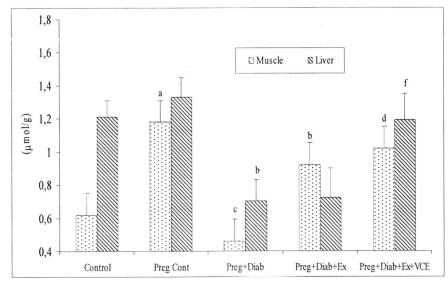

^{a} p<0.05, ^{b} p<0.01 and ^{c} p<0.001 vs group control or preg Cont. ^{d} p<0.05 and ^{f} p<0.001 vs group Preg+Diab+Ex.

Figure 6. The effects of exercise and vitamin C and E (VCE) supplementation on β- carotene concentration in muscle and liver of diabetic pregnant rats. (mean ± SD, n=10).

CONCLUSION

In conclusion, our results suggest that responses of the brain to oxidative stress by diabetes are quite different from those in liver and muscle and the beneficial effect of exercise with a dietary VCE on glutathione and antioxidant system by STZ, up-regulation of GSH-Px, β- carotene and vitamins A and E levels in the liver and muscle. The moderate exercise training with a VCE supplementation may play a role in preventing diabetic oxidative toxic demage of brain, muscle and liver of diabetic pregnant animals.

REFERENCES

Akova, B; Sürmen-Gür, E; Gür, H; Dirican, M; Sarandöl, E; Küçükoğlu, S. Exercise induced oxidative stress and muscle performance in healthy women: role of vitamin E supplementation and endogenous oestradiol. *Eur J Appl Physiol* 2001, 84, 141-147.

Atalay M, Laaksonen DE: Diabetes, oxidative stress and physical exercise. *J Sports Sci Med* 2002; 1: 1-14.

Czernichow S, Hercberg S: Interventional studies concerning the role of antioxidant vitamins in cardiovascular diseases: A review. *J Nutr Health Aging* 2001; 5: 188-195.

Damasceno DC, Volpato GT, Calderon IMP, Rudge MVC.: Oxidative stress and diabetes in pregnant rats. *Anim Rep Sci* 2002; 72: 235-244.

Desai ID. Vitamin E analysis methods for animal tissues. *Methods Enzymol* 1984; 105: 138-147.

Halliwell B, Gutteridge JM. Protection against in biological systems: the superoxide theory of oxygen toxicity. Halliwell B, Gutteridge JM (Eds). In Free radicals in biology and medicine. Oxford, UK. *Clarendon Press*, 1996, pp 86-187.

Kedziora-Kornatowska, K; Szram, S; Kornatowski, T; Szadujkis-Szadurski, L; Kedziora, J; Bartosz, G. Effects of vitamin E and vitamin C supplementation on antioxidantive state and renal glomerular basement membrane thickness in diabetic kidney. *Nephron Exp Nephrol* 2003, 95, 134-143.

Kinalski, M; Sledziewski, A; Telejko, B; Zarzycki, W; Kinalska, I. Antioxidant therapy and streptozotocin-induced diabetes in pregnant rats. *Acta Diabetol* 1999, 36, 113-117.

Kutlu, M; Nazıroğlu, M; Yılmaz, T; Kükner, AŞ: Moderate exercise with a dietary vitamins C and E combination counteracts oxidative stress in kidney and lens of streptozotocin- induced diabetic rat. *Int J Vitam Nutr Res* 2005, 75, 71-80.

Lawrence, RA; Burk, RF. Glutathione peroxidase activity in selenium-deficient rat liver. *Biochem Biophys Res Commun* 1976, 71, 952-958.

Lee, DM; Hoffman, WH; Carl, GF; Khichi M; Cornwell, PE. Lipid peroxidation and antioxidant vitamins prior to, during, and after correction of diabetic ketoacidosis. *J Diabetes Complications.* 2002, 16, 294-300.

Liu, J; Yeo, HC; Overvik-Douki, E; Hagen, T; Doniger, SJ; Chyu, DW; Brooks, GA; Ames, BN. Chronically and acutely exercised rats: biomarkers of oxidative stress and endogenous antioxidants. *J Appl Physiol.* 2000, 89, 21-28.

Lowry, OH; Rosebrough, NJ; Farr, AL; Randall RJ. Protein measurement with the Folin- Phenol reagent. *J Biol Chem* 1951, 193, 265-275.

Mastaloudis, A; Leonard, SW; Traber, MG. Oxidative stress in athletes during extreme endurance exercise. *Free Radic Biol. Med* 2001, 31, 911-922.

Meydani, M; Ewans, W; Handelman G; Biddle, L; Fielding RA; Meydani, SN; Burrill, J; Fiatarone, ME; Blumberg, JB; Cannon, JG. Protective effect of vitamin E on exercise-induced oxidative damage in young and older adults. *Am J Physiol* 1993, 264, R992-998.

Nazıroğlu, M. Enhanced testicular antioxidant capacity in streptozotocin induced diabetic rats: Protective role of vitamins C, E and selenium. *Biol Trace Elem Res* 2003, 94, 61-71.

Nazıroğlu, M; Çay, M. Protective role of intraperitoneally administered vitamin E and selenium on the antioxidative defense mechanism in rats with diabetes induced streptozotocin. *Biol Trace Elem Res* 2001, 79, 149-159.

Nazıroğlu, M; Şimşek, M; Kutlu, M. Moderate exercise with dietary vitamin C and E combination protects streptozotocin- induced oxidative damage to the blood and improves fetal outcomes in pregnant rats. *Clin Chem Lab Med* 2004a, 42, 511-517.

Nazıroğlu, M; Şimşek, M; Şimşek, H; Aydilek, N; Özcan, Z; Atılgan, R. Effects of hormone replacement therapy, vitamin C and E supplementation on antioxidants levels, lipid profiles and glucose homeostasis in postmenopausal women with Type 2. *Clin Chim Acta* 2004b, 344, 63-71.

Nazıroğlu, M; Butterworth, PJ. Protective effects of moderate exercise with dietary vitamin C and E on blood antioxidative defense mechanism in rats with streptozotocin-induced diabetes. *Can J Appl Physiol.* 2005, 30, 172-185.

Packer, L; Landvik, S. Vitamin E in biological systems. In: I. Emerit, L. Packer and C. Auclair (eds). Antioxidants in therapy and preventive medicine. New York: *Plenum Press.* 1990; pp 93-104.

Placer, ZA; Cushman, L; Johnson, BC. Estimation of products of lipid peroxidation (malonyl dialdehyde) in biological fluids. *Anal Biochem* 1966, 16, 359-364.

Radak, Z; Kaneko, T; Tahara, S; Nakamoto, H; Ohno, H; Sasvari, M; Nyakas, C; Goto, S. The effects of exercise training on oxidative damage of lipids, proteins, and DNA in rat skeletal muscle: Evidence for beneficial outcomes. *Free Radic Biol Med* 1999, 27, 69-74.

Sedlak, J; Lindsay, RHC. Estimation of total, protein bound and non-protein sulfhydryl groups in tissue with Ellmann' s reagent. *Anal Biochem* 1968, 25, 192-205.

Siman, CM; Eriksson UJ: Vitamin E decreases the occurrence of malformations in the offspring of diabetic rats. *Diabetes* 1997a; 46: 1054-1061.

Siman, CM; Eriksson, UJ: Vitamin C supplementation of the maternal diet reduces the rate of malformation in the offspring of diabetic rats. *Diabetologia.* 1997b; 40: 416-424.

Suzuki, J; Katoh, N. A simple and cheap method for measuring vitamin A in cattle using only a spectrophotometer. *Jpn J Vet Sci* 1990, 52, 1282-1284.

Takanami, T; Iwane, H; Kawai, Y; Shimomitsu, T. Vitamin E supplementation and endurance exercise; Are there benefits? *Sports Med* 2000, 29, 73-83.

Uriu-Hare, JY; Keen, CL; Applegate, EA; Stern JS. The influence of moderate exercise in diabetic and normal pregnancy on maternal and fetal outcome in the rat. *Life Sci* 1989, 45, 647-654.

Vanheest, JL; Rodgers, CD. Effects of exercise in diabetic rats before and during gestation on maternal and neonatal outcomes. *Am J Physiol* 1997, 273, E727-E733.

Viana, M; Castro, M; Barbas, C; Herrera, E; Bonet, B. Effect of different doses of vitamin E on the incidence of malformations in pregnant diabetic rats. *Ann. Nutr. Metab.* 2003, 47, 6-10.

Yadav, P; Sarkars, S; Bhatnagar, D. Action of capparis deciduas against alloxan-induced oxidative stress and diabetes in rat tissues. *Pharmacol Res* 1997, 36, 221-228.

INDEX

E

F

G

M

N

O

Q

R

S

T

U

V

W

Y